DENNIS & GNASHER

THE WORLD'S WILDEST BOY... AND HIS BEST FRIEND!

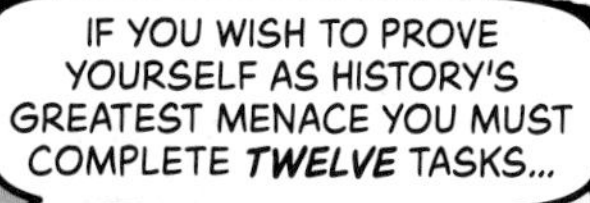

SEVEN THEN!
ONE A DAY? BUT THAT LEAVES ME WITH NO GAMING TIME!
FOUR CHALLENGES!
HOW DOES THAT SOUND?!
FOUR SOUNDS GREAT.
YOUR FIRST CHALLENGE IS TO SLAY THE NEMEON LION.
IT IS NOT! I DON'T CARE WHO YOU ARE, MY BABY ISN'T SLAYING ANYTHING!
OKAY, OKAY! TAME THE LION, THEN PROVE YOUR MENACE POWER BY DOING SOME MISCHIEF WITH IT.
THE NEMEON LION HAS MAGICALLY APPEARED IN BEANOTOWN. JUST FOLLOW THE SCREAMS.
ARRGH!
SO...
HOW HARD CAN IT BE TO TAME A LION?
ARRGH!
YIKES! HERMES NEVER MENTIONED IT WAS GIANT-SIZED!
IT'S JUST A BIG CAT. GET AFTER IT, GNASHER!
GRR!
BELOWS
ARRGH!
I'M GNOT AN IDIOT!
I'VE GOT A PLAN!
I'M ALL EARS!
RUN!
I LIKE IT!

SURPRISE! IT LOOKS LIKE YOU'RE NOT THE FAMOUS MENACE YOU CLAIM TO BE!
YOUR CHALLENGE ISN'T FAIR! NO-ONE CAN TAME SOMETHING THAT LARGE!
HA-HA! YOU'VE NEVER MET A TRICKSTER GOD BEFORE, HAVE YOU?
I WOULDN'T BE A TRICKSTER IF THE CHALLENGES WERE FAIR!
COME ON, GNASHER. WE'RE TAMING THAT LION!
IT'S JUST A BIG CAT, HOW HARD CAN IT BE?
BUT I'M GNOT AN IDIOT!
THE ARMY HAS BEEN CALLED IN TO FIGHT THE LION...
HOP!
NO! I DON'T WANT TO HAVE TO FIGHT THE ARMY AND TAME THE LION!
BOOM
ZAVVI
WOOLWOR
I'M LOVING THIS!
THAT WAS MY SHOP!
SORRY! THE LION WON'T KEEP STILL!
I'VE GOT IT!
WHAT? WHERE?!
BACK HOME...
JUDGING BY THE SCREAMS, YOU HAVEN'T TAMED THE LION YET.
I'M WORKING ON IT!
Mi HERO
DENNIS'S AWESOME JUNK
AHA!
A PEN?!
AT BEANOTOWN ZOO...
HEY NOW, BIG GUY. LET'S TALK ABOUT THIS!
HERE, KITTY!
A LASER PEN!

ANIMAL HOUSE
HYENA HUT
ARMADILLO APARTMENT
POOP
HUH?!
CAN'T... RESIST...
POUNCE!
WOW!
AND NOW FOR THE MISCHIEF PART!
POUNCE!
HA-HA!
IS IT STILL FOLLOWING THE LIGHT?
JUST KEEP RUNNING!
OH LOOK! THE BEAM'S ON THE SCHOOL!
POUNCE
CRASH!
WHERE'D IT GO? SOME OF THE SCHOOL IS STILL STANDING!
VERY CLEVER, DENNIS. YOU TAMED THE NEMEON LION AND MANAGED A SPOT OF MISCHIEF ALONG THE WAY. BUT YOU'RE SURE TO FAIL THE NEXT CHALLENGE!
WHAT IF I PASS ALL THE CHALLENGES? WHAT THEN?
POP
YOU'LL GET A GOLDEN CATAPULT.
GOT ONE.
A GOLDEN PEA-SHOOTER.
GOT ONE.
A GOLDEN JUMPER.
I ONLY WEAR RED AND BLACK JUMPERS!
YOU'LL GET A GOLDEN JUMPER!
I'D LOVE ONE!
THE CHALLENGES CONTINUE LATER IN THE ANNUAL... - ED

MENACE TEST I

IN ORDER TO PROVE YOURSELF A MENACE AS TRUE AS DENNIS, YOU MUST COMPLETE SOME TASKS! HERE IS TASK ONE!

Make your own cannon!

YOU'LL NEED
- BALLOON
- TOILET ROLL TUBE
- STICKY TAPE
- NEWSPAPER

1

Cut off the neck of the balloon and put the balloon round the top of the toilet roll tube.

2

Tape the balloon to the toilet roll tube.

3

Rip the newspaper into little pieces and scrunch into balls. These are your ammo!

4

WARNING! Do not shoot these at people or animals, and only use outside!

Put the scrunched up newspaper balls into the tube. Pull the balloon back then let go and watch them fly!

THE ORDINARY GIRL WITH THE EXTRAORDINARY BEST FRIEND!

ONE HOSE DOWN LATER...
IT LOOKS AS GOOD AS NEW. HELP ME GET IT BACK INTO THE HOUSE.
THUNK!
SLUUUURK!
OVER HERE, YETI.
CRUMP!
SMASH!
STEADY! WE'RE NEARLY THERE!
PERFECT. YOU'D NEVER KNOW THERE WAS EVER A STAIN ON THAT SOFA!
YUP... DAD WILL NEVER SUSPECT A THING!
HR

WHEN LITTLE ERIC EATS A BANANA, HE BECOMES...
BANANAMAN
BEANOTOWN! YOUR GREATEST VILLAINS HAVE ESCAPED FROM PRISON! GENERAL BLIGHT, DOCTOR GLOOM, THE WEATHERMAN AND, ER...
...UM...
APPLEMAN! YOU KNOW ME - YOU CAME TO MY BIRTHDAY PARTY!
BEANO TOWN PRISON
MY HEAD IS A BIG APPLE. IT SHOULDN'T BE HARD TO REMEMBER!
SORRY.
YOU'LL HAVE PLENTY OF TIME TO LEARN EACH OTHER'S NAMES IN PRISON, EVILDOERS!
BANANAMAN!
OH, YOU REMEMBER HIS NAME!
MWAH-HA-HA! BANANAMAN, PREPARE FOR YOUR...
...GREATEST EVER BATTLE!
IS THERE ANYTHING SPECIFIC I SHOULD BE DOING TO PREPARE?
MAYBE STRETCHING OR SOMETHING?
SOMEONE JUST PUNCH HIM!
OKAY.
WAIT... WHAT?!
SO...
OOF! DO YOU HAVE SHARKS FOR FISTS?!
WHAM!
YES! THIS IS YOUR GREATEST BATTLE, SO WE ALL GOT UPGRADES!
CHOMP!
PUNCH!
THIS IS A PRETTY GOOD FIGHT...

...BUT THIS ISN'T REALLY A GREAT **BATTLE.**
BOFF!
OOF!

WE HAVEN'T EVEN STARTED YET! WEATHERMAN, SHOW HIM WHAT YOU'VE GOT!
THIS IS A LITTLE SOMETHING I CALL...

...THE BIGGEST HAILSTONES EVER!

OW! STONE THE CROWS, THAT HURTS!
WHUMP!
THUMP!

HAIL...
GRAB!

...AND FAREWELL!
SMASH!
OH, BOTTOMS!

GO GET HIM, EGGMAN!
IT'S **APPLEMAN!** LOOK, I EVEN HAVE A BIG 'A' ON MY BELT!

IT'S TIME TO UNLEASH MY NEW SPECIAL MOVE - THE **APPLELANCHE!**
SOUNDS TASTY!

AN **AVALANCHE** OF APPLES! GET IT?
WHUMP!

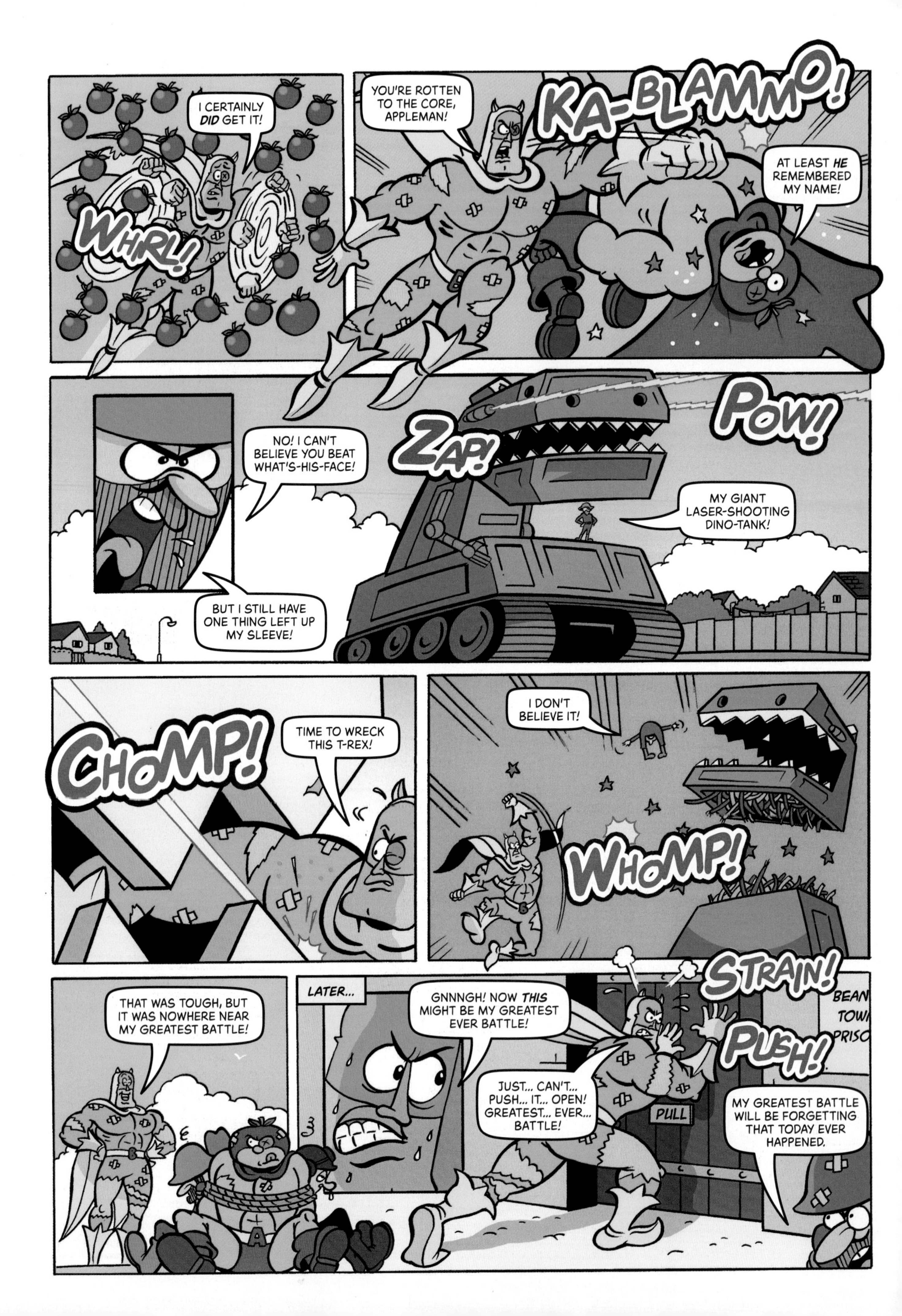
I CERTAINLY DID GET IT!
WHIRL!
YOU'RE ROTTEN TO THE CORE, APPLEMAN!
KA-BLAMMO!
AT LEAST HE REMEMBERED MY NAME!
NO! I CAN'T BELIEVE YOU BEAT WHAT'S-HIS-FACE!
BUT I STILL HAVE ONE THING LEFT UP MY SLEEVE!
ZAP!
POW!
MY GIANT LASER-SHOOTING DINO-TANK!
CHOMP!
TIME TO WRECK THIS T-REX!
I DON'T BELIEVE IT!
WHOMP!
THAT WAS TOUGH, BUT IT WAS NOWHERE NEAR MY GREATEST BATTLE!
LATER...
GNNNGH! NOW THIS MIGHT BE MY GREATEST EVER BATTLE!
STRAIN!
PUSH!
JUST... CAN'T... PUSH... IT... OPEN! GREATEST... EVER... BATTLE!
PULL
MY GREATEST BATTLE WILL BE FORGETTING THAT TODAY EVER HAPPENED.

MINNIE THE MINX

SHE'S TOUGHER THAN ALL THE BOYS...

SO...
WHO AM I KIDDING? I DON'T THINK MUM AND DAD EVEN KNOW WHAT THE INTERNET IS! CHORTLE!

MINNIE! WE NEED TO HAVE A WORD WITH YOU!
IS THE WORD 'PRESENTS', BY ANY CHANCE?
HMPH! MOST DEFINITELY ***NOT!***

CAN YOU EXPLAIN ***THIS***, MINNIE?
GOING INTO THE WEEKEND LIKE
AND DON'T YOU DARE SAY 'IT'S A LAPTOP!'

THIS PICTURE IS EVERYWHERE! YOUR GRAN EVEN SENT ME THIS ONE!
THAT PERSON THINKS I'M FIERCE - AWESOME!
This girl is FIERCE!

IT IS ***NOT*** AWESOME! GO TO YOUR ROOM, YOUNG LADY!
BAH!
I'M SO ASHAMED!

NEXT MORNING...
IT'S A BRAND NEW DAY! I'M SURE THE INTERNET WILL HAVE MOVED ON TO SOMETHING ELSE NOW AND THINGS CAN GET BACK TO...

LOOK! THERE SHE IS!
IT'S THE TROUSER TOMATO GIRL! YAY!
GOING INTO THE WEEKEND LIKE
...NORMAL?!
CAN YOU CATAPULT SOMETHING AT ME, PLEASE?

CAN YOU SIGN MY TOMATO?
ER... SURE!

MUCH SIGNING LATER...
PHEW! THAT WAS WEIRD!
TIME TO GET BACK TO MINXING! AND I SPY A PERFECT TARGET!
THE TROUSER TOMATO GIRL SPLATTED ME! THIS IS THE BEST DAY OF MY LIFE!
NICE TRY, MIN! I'M OUTTA HERE!
HEY! YOU SPOILED MY SHOT!
SPLAT!
CAN I GET A SELFIE WITH YOU?
CAN YOU ENGRAVE MY CATAPULT?
TROUSER TOMATO GIRL! WE AT WIDL WERE THINKING YOU SHOULD USE WIDL-BRAND TOMATOES FOR THE JUICIEST, MESSIEST IMPACTS!
widl
ENOUGH! MY NAME IS MINNIE, NOT TROUSER TOMATO GIRL! THERE'S MORE TO ME THAN TOMATOES! STOP CRAMPING MY STYLE!
THAT'S SO TROUSER TOMATO GIRL!
I KNOW, RIGHT? SHE IS LIT!
I SEE YOU'VE BEEN UP TO YOUR OLD TRICKS AGAIN!
SIGH! BEING INTERNET FAMOUS IS RUBBISH.
YOU'RE COMING HOME RIGHT NOW, YOUNG LADY!
BAH! FOILED AGAIN!
BOO! LEAVE TROUSER TOMATO GIRL ALONE!
WAAH! WHO LEFT THAT THERE?
THIS IS GOING TO GET BIG NUMBERS ONLINE!
CLICK!
SLIP!
HEY! IT'S SLIPPERY TOMATO GUY!
SIGN MY TOMATO!
DO THAT FALLING OVER THING AGAIN!
LEAVE ME ALONE! GET AWAY!
HEE-HEE! ENJOY YOUR FAME, DAD! CONSIDER IT A GIFT FROM MEME TO YOU!

ROGER THE DODGER

HE'S ALWAYS GOT A TRICK UP HIS SLEEVE!

LATER...
DAD! I SAW A BIG ANGRY BEAR. WE SHOULD GET OUT OF HERE!
NICE TRY, ROGER. THERE ARE NO BEARS IN BEANOTOWN WOODS.
LATER THAT NIGHT...
BRR! I'M SO HUNGRY AND I'M FREEZING.
GRR! IT'S YOUR FAULT FOR LEAVING OUR BLANKETS AND COOKING EQUIPMENT BACK IN THE CAR.
LATER STILL...
PERFECT FOR DODGE 598BR. DAD ALWAYS HAS HIS TEDDY BEAR WITH HIM, NO MATTER WHERE WE GO.
ZIP!
WHERE ARE YOU GOING?
JUST THE CALL OF NATURE. I NEED TO GO FOR A WEE.
THIS RECORDING SHOULD SCARE HIM BACK TO THE CAR...
GRRR!
...AND BACK TO A TV AND NICE WARM BED.
ROGER, IT'S A B-B-BEAR!
RUN FOR YOUR LIFE! BACK TO THE CAR!
RIP!
HA-HA. IF YOU GO DOWN TO THE WOODS TODAY, YOU'RE SURE OF A BIG SURPRISE.
BUT...
HA-HA! UN-BEAR-LIEVABLE. HE FELL FOR IT.
HA-HA! HE GOT HIM GOOD.
ARRGH! REAL B-B-BEARS!
LOOK AT HIM GO!
WHERE'S HE OFF TO?
WAIT FOR ME, DAD. I CAN'T BEAR IT OUT HERE ANY MORE!

RUNNING WILD!

Help Dad and Roger find their way out of the woods! Make sure to avoid the bears!

BILLY WHIZZ The fastest boy in the world!

BIFFO THE BEAR Sillier than the average bear!

GNASHER & GNIPPER Beanotown's menace hounds!

LORD SNOOTY Beanotown's billionaire boy!

Rubi
JJ
PIE FACE!

AT THE TREETOP DEN IN BEANOTOWN WOODS...
I'M LOOKING FOR CONTESTANTS FOR MY NEW SHOW - 'MY PET AND ME'.
YOU AND YOUR PET WILL ANSWER THREE QUESTIONS, AND THE ANSWERS HAVE TO MATCH UP.
BRING YOUR PET! GREAT PRIZES TO BE WON! TOWN HALL - TOMORROW!

OOH - I COULD TAKE PAUL. WE COULD BE FAMOUS!
BUT HOW WILL THEY KNOW THE PETS' ANSWERS?

DOCTOR PFOOFLEPFEFFER'S PATENTED PET TRANSLATOR MEANS WE CAN LEARN YOUR PET'S INNERMOST THOUGHTS!
I GUESS THAT EXPLAINS IT! - ED

THE NEXT DAY, AT BEANOTOWN TOWN HALL...
OH MY! SURELY YOU'RE NOT GOING TO ENTER 'MY PET AND ME' WITH A VEGETABLE?
HEY! I KNOW EVERYTHING ABOUT PAUL, WALTER!

I'VE NO DOUBT HE KNOWS MORE THAN YOU, PIE FACE!
GRR! YOU'VE GOT TO BEAT WALTER TO THE PRIZE!

CHECK OUT BERTIE, JJ. HE'S WALTER'S BEST MATE. I WONDER WHY HE'S ACTING SO SUSPICIOUSLY.
I'LL FOLLOW HIM. YOU TWO GO WITHOUT ME.

HIDE THIS UNDER A HAT, WALTER. DOCTOR PFOOFLEPFEFFER SAYS IT'LL READ CLAWDIA'S THOUGHTS AND BEAM THEM STRAIGHT INTO YOUR MIND.
EXCELLENT! I CAN'T LOSE!

WALTER'S GOING TO USE A PET TRANSLATOR TO READ CLAWDIA'S MIND.
THAT'S CHEATING!
I MIGHT BE ABLE TO HELP WITH THAT.

I SHOULD BE ABLE TO HACK THE HELMET'S SIGNAL. WALTER WILL BE IN FOR A SURPRISE.

THE SHOW BEGINS...
WELCOME TO MY NEW SHOW - 'MY PET AND ME'! OUR CONTESTANTS MUST ANSWER QUESTIONS ABOUT THEIR PET AND HOPE THEIR ANSWERS MATCH THEIR PETS'! LET'S START WITH CONTESTANT NUMBER ONE...
...WALTER AND CLAWDIA.

WHAT IS CLAWDIA'S FAVOURITE FOOD?
COME ON, DEVICE. DO YOUR THING.

MEANWHILE...
AHA! CRACKED IT!

FZZT!
OO-ER!

PURRR!

HA-HA! WALTER THINKS HE'S A CAT!
I CHANGED IT SO IT DIDN'T JUST READ MINDS, IT SWAPPED THEM!

MOVING SWIFTLY ON TO OUR NEXT CONTESTANT, PIE FACE AND PAUL... THE POTATO?
HELLO, GRIZZLY. ME AND PAUL ARE YOUR BIGGEST FANS. AFTER DENNIS!

PIE FACE ANSWERS THE FIRST TWO QUESTIONS CORRECTLY...
IT'S ALL RIDING ON YOUR FINAL ANSWER...
IS IT HAWAII?

YES - THAT'S RIGHT! NO-ONE KNOWS THEIR PET LIKE YOU KNOW YOUR POTATO!
YOUR PRIZE IS A YEAR'S SUPPLY OF PET FOOD...

...IF YOU CAN CLAIM IT FROM WALTER.
WOO-HOO!
WE DID ALL THIS FOR PET FOOD?! PAUL DOESN'T EVEN EAT!
PET FOOD
HISS!

THE BASH STREET KIDS
THE CLASS EVERY TEACHER DREADS...

I'M ANNE FINELEY AND I'M HERE AT POSH STREET SCHOOL TO TALK TO MR FOTHERINGTON-BLYTHE WHO HAS BEEN NOMINATED FOR THE BEANOTOWN TEACHER OF THE YEAR AWARD - AGAIN!

MR FOTHERINGTON-BLYTHE, THIS IS THE TENTH YEAR YOU'VE BEEN NOMINATED. AFTER WINNING THE PAST NINE, YOU'VE GOT TO FEEL GOOD ABOUT YOUR CHANCES.
WELL, OF COURSE! I AM THE SUPERIOR EDUCATOR IN THIS TOWN!

ARE YOU LOOKING FORWARD TO THE CEREMONY?
I CANNOT SAY I'M TOO THRILLED. AFTER ALL, IT'S BEING HELD...

'...AT BASH STREET SCHOOL!'
BEST TEACHER AWARD 2021
CAREFUL WITH THAT SIGN, JANITOR! 'ERBERT! LOOK WHERE YOU'RE GOING! SMIFFY, WHAT ON EARTH ARE YOU DOING?
PUSH!
ERK!
YOU SAID YOU WANTED A RED CARPET SO I'M PAINTING THIS ONE!

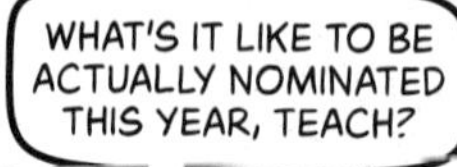
WHAT'S IT LIKE TO BE ACTUALLY NOMINATED THIS YEAR, TEACH?

WE'VE SORTED OUT THE CHAIRS, SIR!

IT'S LOVELY! PEOPLE LIKE ME DON'T USUALLY GET NOMINATED, WE JUST QUIETLY GET ON WITH THE JOB AND...

CRASH!
...EEK! WHAT NOW?!

YOU WERE SUPPOSED TO BE HOLDING THAT!
I WAS ON A BREAK! CHOMP!
THIS IS GOING TO BE A DISASTER!
TOPPLE!
CRISPS
PTCHEE!
CRASH!
BITE!
STIR!
RED

THAT EVENING...
HERE WE ARE! WHAT AN EXCITING EVENING, EH?
WHAT'S HAPPENED TO THAT STATUE? TYPICAL BASH STREET! SNIFF!

MAYOR BROWN, HOW WONDERFUL TO SEE YOU! DID YOU DO SOMETHING WITH YOUR HAIR? HAVE YOU POLISHED YOUR GLASSES?
HELLO, TEACHER.

READY TO WATCH ME WIN ANOTHER AWARD? HAW-HAW!
BAH. HELLO, BLYTHE.
TAP!

WHAT IS THIS, LITTLE GIRL?
SIP!
SIP!
JUST SOME LEMONADE...

URRGH! IT'S SO SOUR!
AND THERE'S A HINT OF SPROUT!
THE CHEEK OF IT! YOU'RE THE SOUR ONES!
...MADE BY OLIVE!

AND...
THANK YOU, SCRUFFY CHILD.
PLEASE TAKE A SEAT!
CURTSEY!

WAAH!
EGAD!
PARP!
PUMP!
TEE-HEE! THEY SOUND REALLY PUMPED FOR THE SHOW!
IT'S GOING TO BE A GAS! CHORTLE!

AHEM! LET'S JUST BEGIN, SHALL WE?
HE CAN'T CONTROL HIS PUPILS!
THAT'S WHY HE WEARS GLASSES! HAW-HAW!

PLUG! I'VE FORGOTTEN THE ENVELOPES WITH THE WINNERS' NAMES IN THEM! CAN YOU GET THEM?
YOU GOT IT, TEACH!

THERE WE GO, BLYTHE... THE RESULTS ARE SWITCHED. YOUR UNBROKEN RUN OF WINS CONTINUES! I'LL BE GIVING OUT THE AWARD, SO YOU CAN'T LOSE!
I CAN'T BELIEVE THEY WERE GOING TO LET TEACHER WIN! THE MAN'S A FOOL!
GASP! I'VE GOT TO TELL THE GANG!

SO...
TEACHER WAS GOING TO WIN, BUT THE MAYOR AND BLYTHE HAVE SWITCHED THE RESULTS!
NO-ONE MESSES WITH TEACH EXCEPT US!
DON'T WORRY - I'VE GOT A PLAN.

AND...
IT NOW BRINGS ME GREAT PLEASURE TO PRESENT THE BEST TEACHER AWARD! AND THE WINNER IS...
I CAN'T WAIT FOR THIS SURPRISE! CHUCKLE!

...OOYAH!
NOW THAT WAS A SURPRISE! CHORTLE!
PRANG!
WHAT HAVE YOU DONE?!

THEY WERE TRYING TO FIX THE AWARD, TEACH! YOU WERE SUPPOSED TO WIN!
I... I WAS?!
UH-OH! TIME WE RETREATED!
ABSOLUTELY! WE'VE STILL GOT THIS!
EXIT
TIP TOE!

AN AWARD IS STILL AN AWARD, NO MATTER HOW ONE GETS IT!
WE COULDN'T HAVE HIM WIN! STANDARDS WOULD...

...SLIP! ARRGH!
DO YOU MIND? I'M STILL PAINTING HERE!
WAAH!
SLIP!
SQUELCH!

I'LL TAKE THAT, THANK YOU VERY MUCH!
I THINK THE MAYOR AND BLYTHE ARE FEELING PRETTY RED-FACED RIGHT ABOUT NOW! CHORTLE!
CATCH!
TEACH IS THE BEST! HOORAY!
DS

CALAMITY JAMES

THE UNLUCKIEST BOY IN THE WORLD!

NUMSKULLS

The Little guys that Live in your head! Everybody has them!

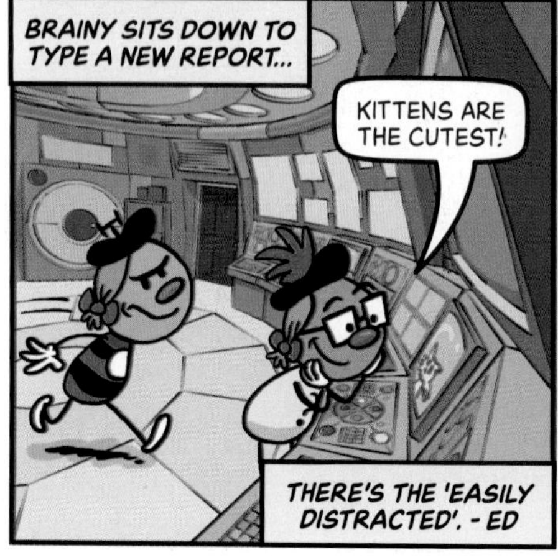

WHAT'S A BETTER WORD FOR MINNIE'S 'OVERREACTY, CARRIED AWAYNESS'?
I'VE FOUND A BUNCH OF GREAT WORDS ON THESAURUS DOT COM. WHAT ABOUT 'ENTHUSIASTIC'?

LOVE IT! COPY AND PASTE LOADS MORE OF THOSE WORDS.
'EAGER', 'EXUBERANT', 'PASSIONATE', 'RABID'.
TAP! TAP! TAP! TAP! TAP!

RABID!
TAP! TAP! TAP! TAP! TAP! TAP! TAP! TAP! TAP! TAP!

HMMM... IT'S STILL NOT PUNCHY ENOUGH. IT NEEDS TO GRAB OUR ATTENTION!
WE NEED PICTURES!

GET THE JAPANESE MEME DOG IN THERE!
WAIT! WHAT IF IT WERE ALL PURE MEMES?!

NO! WAIT AGAIN! I'VE THOUGHT OF SOMETHING EVEN BETTER!

SO...
MUM... DAD... HERE'S MY SCHOOL REPORT...
SCOOL REPORT!
SHERIDAN SMITH AS MINNIE THE MINX
WESTEND
...AS A WEST END MUSICAL!
"HOW IS THIS A THING?" THE TIMES
"CONFUSING!" THE GUARDIAN
DEFINITELY NOT OVERREACTING. AND SHE'S SPELT 'SCHOOL' WRONG! - ED

DENNIS & GNASHER

THE WORLD'S WILDEST BOY... AND HIS BEST FRIEND!

ARRGH!
WHOOOOSH!
I DIDN'T THINK I COULD CLIMB TREES! I GUESS YOU GNEVER KNOW WHAT YOU CAN DO UNTIL YOU'RE BEING CHASED BY A GIANT BOAR!
WE'LL BE SAFE HERE!
CRASH!
I WAS SO VERY WRONG!
ARRGH!
FLIP!
AT LAKE MESS...
SPLASH
HAVING FUN? REMEMBER YOU NEED TO CAUSE MISCHIEF AS WELL OR IT DOESN'T COUNT!
YOU CAN GO RIGHT OFF SOME PEOPLE.
WAIT A MINUTE! I'VE GOT AN IDEA!
POP
DUDE, ARE YOU THE TAP GUY?
YES! NO-ONE TOUCHES THE TAP EXCEPT ME!
ONE TWIST AND THE WATER WILL RUN OUT TO SEA.
DO YOU WANT TO SAVE THE TOWN OR NOT? THERE'S A GIANT BOAR!
I THOUGHT IT WAS A LION?
THAT WAS YESTERDAY!
WE'LL LET THE TAP GUY DO HIS THING WHILE WE GET THE BOAR'S ATTENTION.

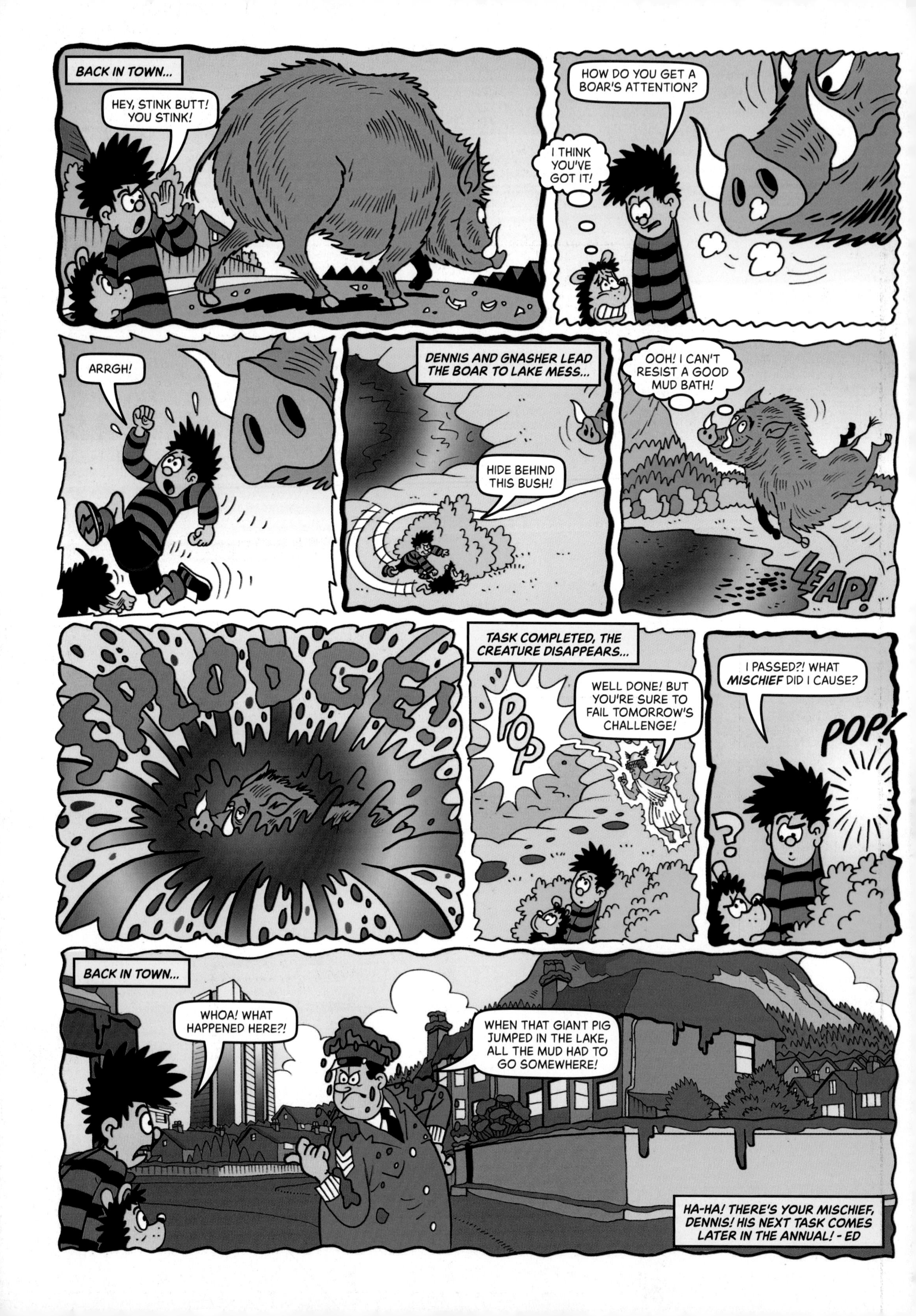
BACK IN TOWN...
HEY, STINK BUTT! YOU STINK!
HOW DO YOU GET A BOAR'S ATTENTION?
I THINK YOU'VE GOT IT!
ARRGH!
DENNIS AND GNASHER LEAD THE BOAR TO LAKE MESS...
HIDE BEHIND THIS BUSH!
OOH! I CAN'T RESIST A GOOD MUD BATH!
LEAP!
SPLODGE!
TASK COMPLETED, THE CREATURE DISAPPEARS...
POP
WELL DONE! BUT YOU'RE SURE TO FAIL TOMORROW'S CHALLENGE!
I PASSED?! WHAT MISCHIEF DID I CAUSE?
POP!
?
BACK IN TOWN...
WHOA! WHAT HAPPENED HERE?!
WHEN THAT GIANT PIG JUMPED IN THE LAKE, ALL THE MUD HAD TO GO SOMEWHERE!
HA-HA! THERE'S YOUR MISCHIEF, DENNIS! HIS NEXT TASK COMES LATER IN THE ANNUAL! - ED

MENACE TEST II

IN ORDER TO PROVE YOURSELF A MENACE AS TRUE AS DENNIS, YOU MUST COMPLETE SOME TASKS! HERE IS TASK TWO!

Make the perfect paper aeroplane!

YOU'LL NEED

- A PIECE OF PAPER

1. Fold the paper in half vertically and unfold to leave a crease. Fold the top corners down to the centre line.

2. Fold the long edges into the centre line and unfold again to leave a crease.

3. Fold your plane along the centre crease, bringing the two outside folds together to make a paper plane shape. Make sure you leave the long edges facing outwards to make your wings. Tape the two outside creases together to complete your plane.

4. Now you're ready for an epic paper plane battle!

MINNIE THE MINX

DON'T WORRY, MIN! I THINK I CAN FIX THIS, I'LL JUST NEED TO REVERSE THE POLARITY.
BZZZZZZZ!
GET REVERSING! I DON'T WANT TO GET TOO...
BZZZZZZZ!
...CARRIED AWAY!
MINNIE!
BZZZZZZZZ!
PING!
PING!
HEY! LET GO! YOU'RE BUGGING ME! PUFF!
BZZZZZZZZZZ!
THAT'S BETTER!
WAIT, NO! THAT'S WORSE! A LOT WORSE! ARRGH!
PLUMMET!
PHEW! SOMETHING BROKE MY FALL! HOW LUCKY AM I?!
WAAH! IT'S SNOT VERY LUCKY AT ALL!
HONK!
URRGH! NOW I KNOW HOW A BOGEY FEELS!

HEY, NERD! NOW THAT LOSER MINNIE HAS GONE, WHY DON'T YOU HELP ME GET A GOOD GRADE ON THIS STUPID ASSIGNMENT?
DO YOU REALLY WANT ME TO TELL YOU WHY NOT, CRUNCHER?

DON'T GET SMART WITH ME!
I THOUGHT YOU WANTED ME TO BE SMART?!
DASH!
HMPH! I'M NOT LETTING CRUNCHER SPEAK TO RUBI LIKE THAT!

HEY! CRUNCHER! THIS IS YOUR CONSCIENCE SPEAKING!
HUH? MY CONSCIENCE SOUNDS LIKE MINNIE!

YOU SHOULD LEAVE RUBI ALONE, YOU BIG BULLY!
OH YEAH? OR WHAT?

OR THIS!
STING!
YIKES! OW! WHAT IS THAT? STOP IT! ARRGH!

WAAH! I'M OUT OF HERE!
UH-OH! NOT AGAIN! ARRGH!
TUMBLE!
ZOOM!

LET'S GET YOU UN-SHRUNK!
PHEW! THANKS, RUBI!
CATCH!

SO...
WHAT DID YOU LEARN FROM YOUR STUDIES?
I LEARNED THAT A LITTLE CAN MAKE A BIG DIFFERENCE! CHUCKLE!
TEE-HEE!

BILLY WHIZZ The fastest boy in the world!

BIFFO THE BEAR Sillier than the average bear!

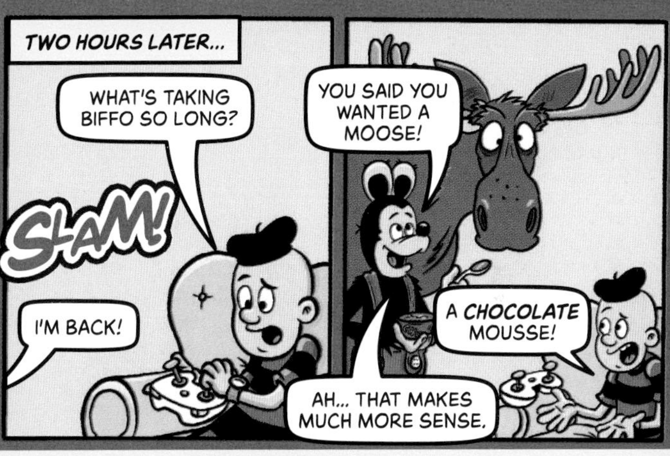

GNASHER & GNIPPER Beanotown's menace hounds!

LORD SNOOTY Beanotown's billionaire boy!

THE ORDINARY GIRL WITH THE EXTRAORDINARY BEST FRIEND!

I KNOW! WE HAD THE ***ALL YOU CAN EAT*** BUFFET AT THIS RESTAURANT!
RESTAURANT
OH, IT'S CLOSED. THAT'S STRANGE. WHY WOULD IT BE CLOSED NOW?
CLOSED FOR THE REST OF THE DAY. NO FOOD LEFT.
YETI EAT EVERYTHING...
I CAN SEE OUR TABLE AND UNICORN ISN'T THERE EITHER. LET'S GO!
BEFORE LUNCH, WE WERE AT HOME SITTING ON THE SOFA!
WAIT A MINUTE...
...YETI, TURN AROUND.
UNICORN!
YOU MUST HAVE SAT ON HIM BEFORE WE EVEN LEFT THE HOUSE AND HE'S BEEN STUCK TO THE FUR ON YOUR BUM ALL DAY!
WELL, I'M GLAD WE GOT TO THE ***BOTTOM*** OF THAT!
HR

Rubi
JJ
PIE FACE!

ARE YOU GOING TO THE DEN TO MEET PIE FACE AS WELL, RUBI?
YEAH, HE SAID IT WAS URGENT.

INSIDE...
THANKS FOR COMING, GUYS. I COULD REALLY USE YOUR HELP WITH SOMETHING.

I SAID I'D LOOK AFTER GALAHAD, BUT IT'S JUST BEEN *EXHAUSTING*.
HUH?

HA-HA!
YEAH, RIGHT! YOU HAD US GOING THERE, PIE FACE!

SO, CAN YOU LOOK AFTER HIM FOR ME?
SURE THING. HOW *TOUGH* CAN IT BE TO LOOK AFTER SOMETHING THAT SLEEPS ALL DAY?

BUT...
HAS THAT REALLY ANNOYING POTATO LEFT? ALL HE DOES IS TALK ABOUT GOING TO HAWAII! IT'S DRIVING ME MAD!
HE'S WAKING UP.

I KNOW JUST THE THING TO KEEP A HAMSTER ENTERTAINED...

I DON'T THINK HAMSTERS LIKE SQUEAKY TOYS, RUBI. BUT *DOGS* DO.
SQUEAK!
SQUEAK!

SEE?
GNICE!

HEY! GIVE THAT BACK! IT'S FOR GALAHAD!
GNOPE!

WHEN MY BROTHER HAD A HAMSTER, HE SAID IT USED TO LOVE RUNNING ON ITS WHEEL.

GIVE IT A SPIN, GALAHAD!
HE DOESN'T SEEM KEEN. WHAT IF I DEMONSTRATE?
TWIRL!

SO...
YOU'RE ALMOST AS WEIRD AS THE BOY WITH THE POTATO!

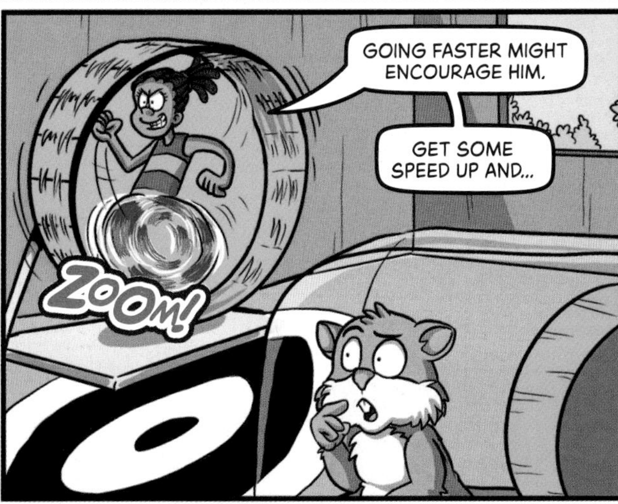
GOING FASTER MIGHT ENCOURAGE HIM.
GET SOME SPEED UP AND...
ZOOM!

...WHOA!
SPIN!

AND...
I... GASP! GOT THE... PANT! TOY BACK!

I NEED A LIE DOWN!
ME TOO!

LATER...
SEE? I TOLD THEM IT WAS EXHAUSTING LOOKING AFTER GALAHAD.

PEDIGREE PUNS!
Galahad's brought Beanotown's pets together for these paw-some jokes!
What is a small dog's favourite city?
New Yorkie!
How did Noah see the animals in the Ark at night?
With floodlighting!
What are caterpillars afraid of?
Dog-erpillars!
What do you do if a cat swallows your pencil?
Use a pen!
What was the first animal in space?
The cow that jumped over the moon!
Where do mice park their boats?
At the hickory dickory dock!
What do you call a pig with no legs?
A ground hog!
What happened to the dog that ate nothing but garlic?
His bark was worse than his bite!
What animal has more lives than a cat?
Frogs – they croak every night!

THE BASH STREET KIDS
THE CLASS EVERY TEACHER DREADS...
PART ONE!

ONE EVENING, IN BEANOTOWN...
LISTEN, BENNY! I KNOW WE'VE JUST MOVED INTO TOWN, BUT WE'VE GOT SOME GOOD NEWS!
WE'VE GOT YOU INTO THE LOCAL SCHOOL!
SCHOOL? BUT SCHOOL SUCKS!
SCUFF!
KITCHEN
LOUNGE

THAT'S TOO BAD! AS SOON AS WE GET THE ACCEPTANCE LETTER, YOU'RE GOING!
FINE! SHEESH!

MEANWHILE, ACROSS TOWN...
SIGH! I KNOW I'M SPECIAL... I'VE GOT SOMETHING, SOME SORT OF POWER. I JUST WISH I COULD GET INTO A SCHOOL FOR MAGIC, THEN I'D SHOW EVERYONE!

KEEP IT DOWN IN THERE, TROTTER! AND GET TO BED!
SIGH!

ELSEWHERE...
TWIT-TWOO!
FLAP! FLAP!
CONGRATULATIONS! YOU'VE BEEN ACCEPTED INTO HOGLUMPS' SCHOOL OF MAGIC.

COO! COO!
FLAP! FLAP!
CONGRATULATIONS! YOU'VE BEEN ACCEPTED INTO BASH STREET SCHOOL!

THUD!
TWIT!
WHAP!
COO!

DIVE!
TWIT! TWIT! TWOO!
FLAP!
COO!
FLAP!
GRAB!

TWOO!
DROP!

THE NEXT MORNING...
GOAL!
HEY! CHEAT!
HMM... THIS PLACE DOESN'T SEEM VERY MAGICAL.
YOU LIKE SCHOOL MORE!
NO, YOU DO!
DAZZLE!
SWISH!
TRIP!
BOOT!
ROCK
THUD!
OOFYAH!

CLANG! CLANG!
COME ALONG, GET INSIDE OR I'LL TURN YOU ALL IN TO THE *HEAD*.
BAH! FUN'S OVER!
GASP? DID HE SAY HE'D TURN THEM INTO A HEAD?! HE MUST BE SOME KIND OF GRAND WIZARD!

TODAY WE HAVE A NEW STUDENT JOINING US! I WANT YOU TO BE VERY WELCOMING TO HIM WHEN HE ARRIVES!
POOR KID! WE SHOULD WARN HIM TO RUN WHILE HE STILL CAN!
CHUCKLE!

EEK! THERE YOU ARE! HEAVENS! IT WAS LIKE YOU POPPED OUT OF NOWHERE!
MAYBE I DID, SIR.

WHY DON'T YOU INTRODUCE YOURSELF TO THE CLASS?
HI... I'M TROTTER. PEOPLE CALL ME HAIRY TROTTER, ON ACCOUNT OF, WELL... MY HAIR.
HA-HA! FANCY BEING NAMED AFTER WHAT YOU LOOK LIKE, EH, *SPOTTY?!*

PERHAPS YOU'D LIKE TO TELL US A BIT ABOUT YOURSELF? ANY HOBBIES? HIDDEN TALENTS?
I LIKE *MAGIC*. I'M TRYING TO LEARN SOME.

WE LIKE MAGIC TOO! FATTY HERE CAN MAKE A SAUSAGE ROLL *DISAPPEAR!*
TA-DA!
PLOOP!
SHATTER!
AND PLUG CAN MAKE A MIRROR SHATTER JUST BY LOOKING AT IT!

PERHAPS YOU COULD SHOW US ONE OF YOUR LITTLE MAGIC TRICKS, TROTTER?
CAN YOU MAKE ALL OF THOSE TEXTBOOKS VANISH? CHORTLE!
MAYBE. LET ME SEE NOW...

...*TEXTPELLIARMUS!*
FWOOSH!

WAS, ER... WAS THAT OKAY?
WOW! THEY'VE GONE!

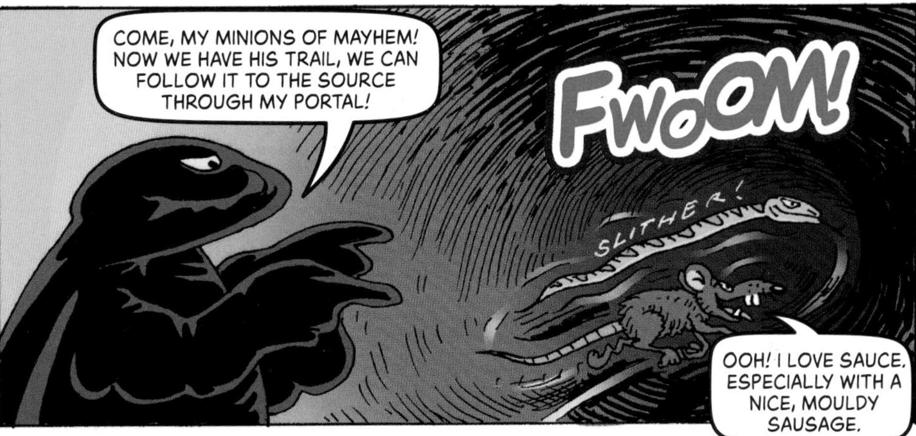

BRING! DRING!

YAY!

WAHOO! BREAK TIME!

TITTER! LOOKSSSS LIKE OLD BALDYMORT IS FEELING A BIT RUN-DOWN! CHUCKLE!

TRAMPLE!

STOMP!

OOF! WATCH IT! HEY, MIND THE ROBE! OUCH!

DS

WILL THE EVIL BALDYMORT CAPTURE HAIRY TROTTER? WHAT WILL BECOME OF THE BASH STREET KIDS? WHERE DID I LEAVE MY SARNIES? FIND OUT THE ANSWERS TO THESE QUESTIONS IN PART TWO! - ED

NUMSKULLS

The Little guys that Live in your head! Everybody has them!

WHAT?
WHAT?

ARRGH! WHAT DO WE DO?! HOW DO YOU DODGE THE ULTIMATE DODGE?!
I KNOW WHAT TO DO!

SORRY, MUM, I CAN'T REVISE. I NEED TO WASH THE CAR!

WHAT DID YOU SAY THAT FOR? THAT'S NOT A DODGE! THAT'S DOING SOMETHING!
I PANICKED!

NO, ROGER, LEAVE THAT. NOTHING'S MORE IMPORTANT THAN YOUR SCHOOLWORK.

PHEW! WE DODGED WASHING THE CAR!
GRRR!

WASHING THE CAR WAS YOUR IDEA!!! WE'RE MEANT TO BE DODGING REVISION!!!

BRING ALL THE COMPUTERS ONLINE! I NEED MAXIMUM THINKING POWER TO DODGE THE DODGE TO END ALL DODGES!

OKAY, MUM. I'LL DO IT NOW.

WAIT, WHAT?
DID I MISS SOMETHING?

OH, THE CLASSIC 'SAY WE WILL BUT DON'T'!
YEAH, DIDN'T REALLY NEED THE COMPUTER!

CALAMITY JAMES

THE UNLUCKIEST BOY IN THE WORLD!

WHEN LITTLE ERIC EATS A BANANA, HE BECOMES...
BANANAMAN

SORRY, DOCTOR GLOOM, BUT I'LL HAVE TO GIVE YOUR ICE ROBOT THE COLD SHOULDER!
SMASH!
BAH!
JUST BECAUSE YOU HAVE SUPERPOWERS, YOU THINK YOU'RE BETTER THAN EVERYONE ELSE, BANANAMAN!
IT'S NOT FAIR!
CRASH!
ER... THIS IS THE BIT WHERE YOU NORMALLY GO TO PRISON.
YOU WON'T BE SO SPECIAL IF I USE MY SUPERPOWER GENERATOR...
CLICK!
CLACK!
...AND GIVE SUPERPOWERS TO EVERYONE IN BEANOTOWN!
MWAH-HA-HA-HA!

LOOK AT ME! I CAN FLY!
THAT MUST BE EXCITING FOR YOU.

MY NEW NAME IS... SUPER-MIN!
NOT VERY ORIGINAL, BUT I SUPPOSE YOU ARE NEW TO THIS.

AND MY SPECIAL MOVE IS THE TOMATO TORNADO!
SPLAT!

PLEASE, MINNIE! STOP! I'M, ERM... NOT HUNGRY?

JUST A MINUTE! THAT'S MY POWER...

...I'M ALWAYS HUNGRY!
CHOMP!
FATTY?
I'M NOT FATTY ANY MORE! I AM...
RRRRIP!
...THE INCREDIBLE BULK!
BULK EAT!
CHOMP!
I DON'T THINK YOU'RE GETTING ENOUGH IRON IN YOUR DIET.
PIE FACE! WHAT ARE YOU DOING UP THERE?
I'M NOT PIE FACE!
I'M THE AMAZING PIE-DERMAN NOW!
THE PIE IS CAST!
THAT'S MY NEW CATCHPHRASE. DO YOU LIKE IT?
SPLAT!
NO.
PIE FACE HAVE PIES? BULK HUNGRY!
NO! THEY'RE FOR SUPERHERO STUFF! LEAVE ME ALONE!
WHAT IS THAT?
THUMP! THUMP!
I AM TOOT!
YES, I KNOW. WE'VE MET.
WATCH WHERE YOU PUT YOUR BRANCHES, WILL YOU?

I AM TOOT!
YOU ALREADY SAID THAT. I THINK IT'S TIME YOU MAKE LIKE A TREE AND *LEAF!*
SWISH!
I THINK YOU SHOULD MAKE LIKE A BANANA... AND *SPLIT!*
FWOOSH!
IT'S ROCKET RUBI AND TOOT!
DOCTOR GLOOM, WHY DID EVERYONE GET DIFFERENT SUPERPOWERS?
I DUNNO. I JUST HIT THE SHUFFLE BUTTON ON THE POWERS GENERATOR!
WHICH MEANS THAT I GET POWERS TOO!
HEY, NEW SUPERHEROES - ASSEMBLE!
IF YOU WANT TO BE SUPERHEROES YOU HAVE TO FIGHT SUPERVILLAINS! THOSE ARE THE RULES!

POW!
BANG!
BIFF!
IT'S SO NICE TO LET SOMEONE ELSE DO THIS FOR A CHANGE!

POW!
SMASH!
HMM... 'BATTLE OR BRAWL'? FIVE LETTERS.

BANG!
ZZZZZZZ!
THUMP!

YOU ONLY BEAT *ONE* OF MY VILLAINS! I'VE GOT *LOADS* OF THEM!
FINALLY! THAT TOOK AGES!

WE'VE DECIDED WE DON'T WANT TO BE SUPERHEROES ANY MORE! IT'S TOO MUCH LIKE *HARD WORK!*
GOOD THING THEY GAVE UP BEFORE THEY BECAME SUPERVILLAINS!
SUPER POWERS OFF

ROGER THE DODGER
HE'S ALWAYS GOT A TRICK UP HIS SLEEVE!
REMEMBER YOU SAID IF WE BEHAVED WHILE YOU WENT SHOPPING YOU'D TAKE US TO BEANOTOWN BURGERS?
YES, ROGER. WE REMEMBER.
AT BEANOTOWN BURGERS...
BURGERS
DRIVE IN
OH NO. IT LOOKS LIKE THE WHOLE TOWN IS HERE.
THERE'S A HUGE QUEUE INSIDE TOO.
LOOKS LIKE WE'LL HAVE TO FINISH OFF THAT CABBAGE SOUP FROM YESTERDAY'S DINNER.
YUCK! WE CAN'T GIVE UP SO QUICKLY.
SO...
WE JUST NEED TO POP INSIDE TO USE THE LOO, MUM.
OKAY, BUT BE QUICK!
WE DO?
WHAT'S GOING ON?!
HEY! WHERE'S THE MANAGER?
WE DON'T KNOW. HE DIDN'T TURN UP FOR WORK THIS MORNING.
I HAVE A KING-SIZE DODGE THAT SHOULD SAVE US.
STAFF ROOM
ALL WE NEED IS A LITTLE DISGUISE.
SO...
THIS SHOULD FOOL THEM.
HEE-HEE. THIS IS A WHOPPER OF A DODGE.
Head Office
YOU CAN'T BE BACK HERE. WHO ARE YOU?
WE'RE FROM HEAD OFFICE.
NO CHANCE. I DON'T BELIEVE YOU.
OH YEAH? LOOK AT THIS.
Head Office
WE'VE BEEN FLIPPING BURGERS SINCE BEFORE YOU WERE BORN, BOY!

SORRY, SIRS.
I WANT A DOUBLE ROYALE WITH CHEESE, EVERYTHING ON THE SIDE AND I WANTED IT 20 SECONDS AGO.
MOVE IT! MOVE IT!
SO...
NOW THAT EVERYTHING IS BACK ON TRACK IT'S TIME TO SERVE UP DODGE 345PB.
BRING US TWO OF EVERYTHING SO WE CAN PERFORM A TASTE TEST.
AND DON'T SCRIMP ON THE SAUCE!
OUTSIDE, THE MANAGER HAS FINALLY ARRIVED...
I CAN'T BELIEVE MY CAR BROKE DOWN AGAIN. I'M SO LATE.
WHAT IS GOING ON HERE?
HEAD OFFICE, SIR. TWO GUYS HAVE COME DOWN TO WHIP US INTO SHAPE.
I WASN'T TOLD ANYONE FROM HEAD OFFICE WAS VISITING TODAY.
THAT'S ODD. I'M SURE THEY EMAILED. NEVER MIND.
HANG ON A MINUTE! THAT MOUSTACHE IS FAKE! YOU'RE NOT FROM HEAD OFFICE!
DAVE! LEG IT!
SLIP!
GET BACK HE...
SQUIRT!
...ARRGH!
SLIP!
BACK AT THE CAR...
YOU WERE GONE A LONG TIME. WE'RE ALMOST AT THE FRONT OF THE QUEUE.
IT'S OKAY. WE AREN'T HUNGRY ANY MORE. LET'S GET OUT OF HERE.
WELL, I'M STARVING.
ME TOO. LET'S ORDER DRIVE-THRU.
HELLO, BOYS!
EEP!
UH-OH! WE'RE IN FOR A GRILLING NOW.

IT'S THE...
BEANOLYMPICS!
A BEANOTOWN ADVENTURE!
BZZZZZZZZ
BZZZZZZZZ

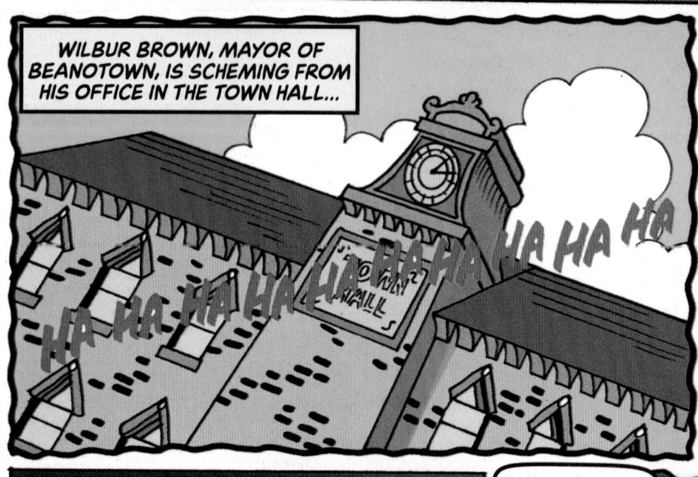
WILBUR BROWN, MAYOR OF BEANOTOWN, IS SCHEMING FROM HIS OFFICE IN THE TOWN HALL...
HA HA HA HA HA HA HA HA HA HA

HIS SON, WALTER, IS JOINING IN...
WHY ARE WE DOING AN EVIL LAUGH?
BECAUSE I HAVE AN EVIL PLAN FOR THE TOWN TO HOST ITS OWN VERSION OF THE OLYMPICS... THE BEANOLYMPICS!
TOP SECRET PLANS
MIDDLE SECRET PLANS

WHAT MAKES IT EVIL THOUGH? ISN'T SPORT GOOD? IT HELPS TO FIGHT OBESITY.
I, ER... DON'T KNOW. I JUST ASSUMED IT WOULD BE EVIL BECAUSE I'D THOUGHT OF IT!

THERE MUST BE A WAY OF MAKING IT EVIL!
IF I, ER... OR WE, UM... NO. I'VE GOT NOTHING!

IT'S EASY! DENNIS WILL FIGURE IT OUT FOR US!
HUH?!

AND SO...
HMM...
BEANOLYMPICS
COMING
SURPRISINGLY
SOON!
BY ORDER
OF THE MAYOR

WHY THE SUSPICIOUS FACE, DENNIS? IT SOUNDS LIKE FUN.
BUT IT'S 'BY ORDER OF THE MAYOR'. EVERYTHING THE MAYOR DOES IS EVIL.

NOT EVERYTHING... YOU CAN'T EAT TOAST EVILLY!
I BET HE CAN! IT MUST BE A COVER FOR SOMETHING ELSE!

IT WOULD BE A GOOD COVER!
SHH!

A COVER FOR WHAT THOUGH?
MAYBE HE'S PLANNING TO STEAL SOMETHING.

HE'S RICH! WHY STEAL THINGS WHEN YOU CAN BUY THEM?
SO... WHAT HE WANTS TO STEAL MUST BE SOMETHING YOU CAN'T BUY. THE MUSEUM IS FULL OF VALUABLE STUFF LIKE THAT!

SUCH AS?
IS THERE ANYTHING YOU WANT FROM THE MUSEUM?
I'M NOT SURE.

HE PROBABLY WANTS THE CRYSTAL SKULL. SOME PEOPLE THINK IT WAS MADE BY ALIENS AND THAT IF ACTIVATED, IT'LL TELL YOU HOW TO MAKE FUTURISTIC ALIEN TECH!

THAT'S IT! WITH FUTURISTIC ALIEN TECH I COULD RULE THE WORLD!

THE MAYOR ISN'T DOING THAT! YOU JUST MADE IT UP!

WHILE EVERYONE IS WATCHING THE GAMES, I'M TOTALLY STEALING THAT SKULL!

THE GAMES BEGIN...
HI! I'M GARY GARYSON AND I'LL BE YOUR HOST FOR THIS YEAR'S BEANOLYMPICS!
IT'S A PACKED SHOW FOR YOU, SO LET'S GO STRAIGHT TO MY CO-HOST, GARY GARYKINSON, FOR THE FIRST EVENT!
MOUNTAIN RUNNING

HI, GARY, I'M IN A HELICOPTER ABOVE MOUNT BEANO, THE LOCATION OF THE RACE TO THE MOUNTAIN TOP!
THAT'S RIGHT, GARY. RUNNERS FROM ACROSS THE GLOBE ARE LINED UP AT THE START.
'ACROSS THE GLOBE', GARY?
NOT REALLY, GARY, JUST BEANOTOWN.
BANG!

ARRGH!
WHOOSH!
WHOOSH!

SORRY! WITH MY BAD LUCK I GET NERVOUS AROUND LOUD BANGS.
IT WASN'T AN ACTUAL BANG, IT WAS JUST ME SHOUTING 'BANG'.
STOP SAYING 'BANG'!

BILLY WHIZZ ZOOMS INTO AN EARLY LEAD...
WHOOOOOOSH!

...AND WINS!
UH-OH.

THAT'S A GOLD IN THE FIRST EVENT, BILLY!
AND NEWS JUST IN, BILLY WHIZZ HAS BEEN BANNED FROM THE OTHER EVENTS TO PREVENT HIM FROM WINNING THEM ALL!

'THE NEXT EVENT IS, ER... THE HIGH DIVE OR TRAMPOLINING.'

IT'S BOTH, GARY! UP FIRST TO TRY THIS INCREDIBLY DANGEROUS-LOOKING SPORT IS FATTY!
WAIT! I'VE CHANGED MY MIND!

WE'LL HAVE TO COME BACK TO THAT EVENT LATER TO CHECK IF FATTY HAS GOT EITHER BRAVER OR STUPIDER!

NEXT UP, GARY, IS BEANOLYMPIC SNAP!
SNAP!
SLAP!

SNAP? REALLY, GARY? THAT'S NOT VERY EXCITING!
I'M THINKING THERE ARE A FEW 'SPORTS' ON THIS LIST WE MIGHT NOT BOTHER COVERING... 'BEANOLYMPIC STARING', 'BEANOLYMPIC STANDING STILL' AND 'CRICKET'.

IN THE CROWD, DENNIS IS KEEPING A CLOSE EYE ON THE MAYOR...
YOUR PLAN TO LET DENNIS THINK UP A PLAN ISN'T WORKING! HE WON'T TAKE HIS EYES OFF ME!

HMM... WE NEED A 'SPORT' THAT WILL DISTRACT DENNIS.
'WELLY BAT' SHOULD DO IT!

IN BEANOLYMPIC WELLY BAT, COMPETITORS MUST HIT A WELLY FULL OF CUSTARD WITH A CRICKET BAT...
SPLAT!
BOSH!
FOUR METRES.
JUDGE
3
4
5

FOUR METRES IS A NEW WORLD RECORD, GARY... BECAUSE IT'S THE FIRST TIME ANYONE HAS PLAYED IT!
WHO'S MAKING UP THESE 'SPORTS', GARY?

BEANOLYMPIC COMMITTEE
UMM...
IDEAS?

IF TOP LEVEL INTERNATIONAL WELLY BAT CAN'T DISTRACT DENNIS, WE NEED SOMETHING WITH MORE BUDGET!

NEXT UP, DRONE RACING!
D-D-DRONES?
GOTTA STAY STRONG!

YOU CAN EITHER COMPETE AS A DRONE PILOT OR...
...BY SHOOTING AT THE DRONES WITH CATAPULTS!
ME! ME!
NO! ME!
ARRGH!
BACK HOME, GNASHER IS GLUED TO THE DRAMA UNFOLDING ON TV...
ZZZZZ
ZZZZ
NOW THE DRONE PILOTS ARE IN PLACE, GARY, IT'S A GOOD TIME TO COVER THE RULES OF THIS EVENT.
INDEED, GARY. THERE AREN'T ANY! IT'S AS IF SOMEONE IS MAKING THIS UP AS THEY GO ALONG!
BZZZZZZ
BZZZZ
BZZZZZZ
THEY'LL NOT HIT MY DRONE. I'M NOT KNOWN AS 'THE DODGER' FOR NOTHING!
YOU'RE KNOWN AS 'THE DODGER' FOR DODGING CHORES!
DODGE THIS, DANNY!
BZZZZZZZ
HEY!
THE MAYOR'S JUST HANDED ME THE RULES, GARY. IT SAYS COMPETITORS MUST 'RACE AROUND THE PLAYGROUND UNTIL HE'S GOT THE THING'.
BANG!
ARRGH!
BZZZZZZZ
BZZZZZ
BZZZZZZ

THE ROUTE GOES ROUND THE ROUNDABOUT, UNDER THE SLIDE, OVER THE SEE-SAW AND THROUGH THE CLIMBING FRAME.

I WASN'T EVEN HOLDING A WATER PISTOL THAT TIME!
GASP!

I'M WORRIED ABOUT OUR ROLE IN THIS EVENT.
WE'LL BE FINE. THEY GAVE US HELMETS.
NO, THEY DIDN'T!

BZZZZZZZZ
ARRGH!

NEARBY...
WHAT ARE YOU DOING UP HERE, FATTY? YOU'RE MISSING THE DRONES!
STOP WOBBLING IT!

MEANWHILE..

NOW THAT EVERYONE, INCLUDING DENNIS, IS BUSY... WE CAN GET THAT SKULL!
SNEAK
SNEAK

HERE THEY COME!
BZZZZZZZ

POW!

PING!
'ROGER'S DRONE HAS BEEN HIT, GARY! HE'S LOST A ROTOR BUT HE'S STILL IN THE AIR!'

'THE DODGER'? HA!

'DANNY'S DRONE HAS BEEN SMASHED ON THE CLIMBING FRAME, GARY!'
SMASH
HA-HA!
GRR!
AT BEANOTOWN MUSEUM...
THERE IT IS, FATHER! NO-ONE'S WATCHING US. WE CAN JUST TAKE IT!
POW!
'MINNIE'S SHOT THE AERIAL OFF PLUG'S DRONE, GARY! IT'S OUT OF CONTROL!'
PING!
WHAT ARE YOU WAITING FOR? JUST TAKE IT!
OLD STUFF
WELL OLD STUFF
SERIOUSLY, HOW OLD?!
!!
I'M TRYING TO MAKE THE MOMENT MORE DRAMATIC WITH A PAUSE!
PLUG'S OUT OF CONTROL DRONE GIVES FATTY A NUDGE...
BZZZZZZZ
ARRGH!
HELP!
BOING!
I THINK THAT'S A BIG ENOUGH DRAMATIC PAUSE NOW!
YOU'RE RIGHT. IT'S NOT LIKE SOMEONE IS JUST GOING TO DROP OUT OF THE SKY AND CATCH US, IS IT?
SNAP!
OOF!
BOSH
SMASH
NO!
SHATTER!

MY DRONE'S THE ONLY ONE LEFT! HAVE I WON?
GASP! I'VE FORGOTTEN ABOUT THE MAYOR!
WHAT ABOUT HIM?

HE'S GOT AN EVIL PLAN TO STEAL THE CRYSTAL SKULL FROM THE MUSEUM SO HE CAN RULE THE WORLD WITH ALIEN INVENTIONS!

ROMANS
VIKINGS
OLD AND DUSTY STUFF
DUSTY AND OLD STUFF
NOT SO FAST, MAYOR!
TOO SLOW, DENNIS! YOUR PLAN FAILED!

MY PLAN?!
IT WAS YOUR IDEA TO STEAL THE SKULL, BUT IT'S BEEN SMASHED TO PIECES.

YOU'RE WORKING FOR THE MAYOR, DENNIS?
IT WAS YOUR IDEA?
NO! I MEAN, I DID HAVE AN IDEA, BUT, ER...
YOUR EVIL SCHEME TO STEAL THE SKULL FAILED THANKS TO FATTY!
SO I'M THE HERO?
COOL!

NEARBY...
WHERE IS EVERYONE? THE NEXT EVENT IS LONG- DISTANCE CAKE JUGGLING!

EVENTUALLY, THE MEDALS ARE HANDED OUT...
AND FOR STOPPING DENNIS'S PLAN...
STOP SAYING IT LIKE THAT!
TOWN HALL

FINALLY, THE GOLD MEDAL FOR SLEEPING THROUGH THE ENTIRE ADVENTURE GOES TO GNASHER!
GNUH?!
NIGEL PARKINSON

THE END

BILLY WHIZZ The fastest boy in the world!

BIFFO THE BEAR Sillier than the average bear!

GNASHER & GNIPPER Beanotown's menace hounds!

LORD SNOOTY Beanotown's billionaire boy!

WHEN LITTLE ERIC EATS A BANANA, HE BECOMES...
BANANAMAN

RECORD 00:12
HELLO, ER... BLIGHT FANS! I'M GENERAL BLIGHT. WELCOME TO MY VLOG!
I'M GENERAL BLIGHT... WAIT, I ALREADY SAID THAT. AND YOU FANS ARE... BLIGHTERS? CAN I CALL YOU THAT?

I DON'T UNDERSTAND WHY WE'RE DOING THIS.
CAN'T WE JUST BLOW STUFF UP LIKE WE USUALLY DO?

NO! I'M GOING TO BE A FAMOUS VLOGGER AND RULE THE WORLD THAT WAY!
BUT YOU DON'T HAVE ANY VIEWERS.

I HAVE TWO VIEWERS RIGHT NOW! AND ONLY ONE OF THOSE IS MY MUM!
UNLESS SHE'S GOT TWO PHONES.

FINE! LET'S MAKE THINGS A BIT MORE EXCITING! WHO WANTS TO SEE ME ROB A BANK?

SO...
WELCOME TO MY 'HOW TO BE A SUPERVILLAIN' CHANNEL.
WHEN ROBBING A BANK, REMEMBER TO ASK FOR BAGS WITH MONEY SIGNS ON THEM.

DON'T BANK ON IT, GENERAL BLIGHT!
SMASH!
EEK! BANANAMAN! RUN AWAY!

HOW DID HE GET THERE SO FAST?
IT'S A MYSTERY!

LATER THAT DAY...
RECORD 00:14
THAT DIDN'T GO VERY WELL. BUT YOU KNOW WHAT ALWAYS WORKS?
A GIANT ROBOT RAMPAGE!

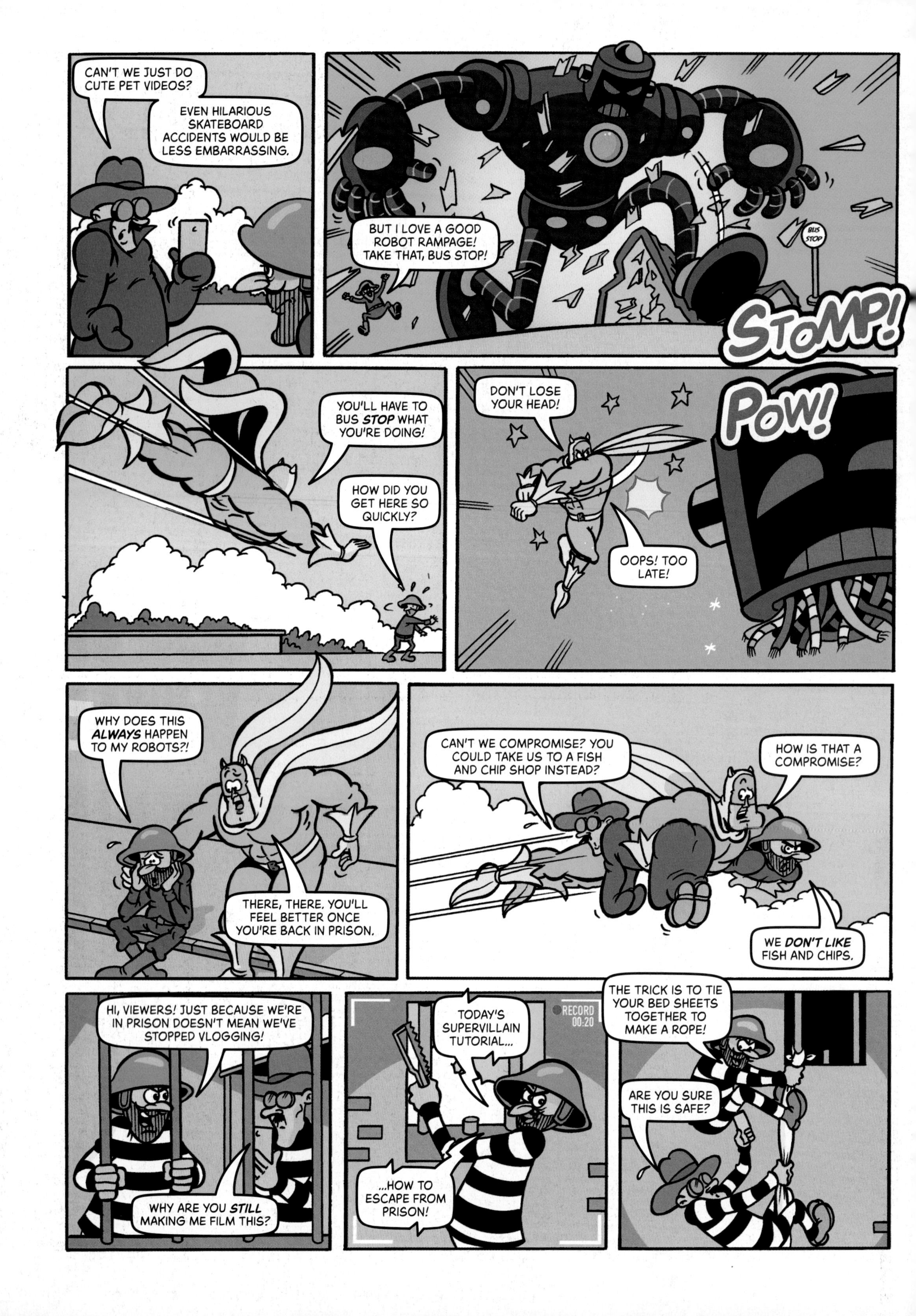
CAN'T WE JUST DO CUTE PET VIDEOS?
EVEN HILARIOUS SKATEBOARD ACCIDENTS WOULD BE LESS EMBARRASSING.
BUT I LOVE A GOOD ROBOT RAMPAGE! TAKE THAT, BUS STOP!
BUS STOP
STOMP!
YOU'LL HAVE TO BUS STOP WHAT YOU'RE DOING!
HOW DID YOU GET HERE SO QUICKLY?
DON'T LOSE YOUR HEAD!
POW!
OOPS! TOO LATE!
WHY DOES THIS ALWAYS HAPPEN TO MY ROBOTS?!
THERE, THERE. YOU'LL FEEL BETTER ONCE YOU'RE BACK IN PRISON.
CAN'T WE COMPROMISE? YOU COULD TAKE US TO A FISH AND CHIP SHOP INSTEAD?
HOW IS THAT A COMPROMISE?
WE DON'T LIKE FISH AND CHIPS.
HI, VIEWERS! JUST BECAUSE WE'RE IN PRISON DOESN'T MEAN WE'VE STOPPED VLOGGING!
WHY ARE YOU STILL MAKING ME FILM THIS?
RECORD 00:20
TODAY'S SUPERVILLAIN TUTORIAL...
...HOW TO ESCAPE FROM PRISON!
THE TRICK IS TO TIE YOUR BED SHEETS TOGETHER TO MAKE A ROPE!
ARE YOU SURE THIS IS SAFE?

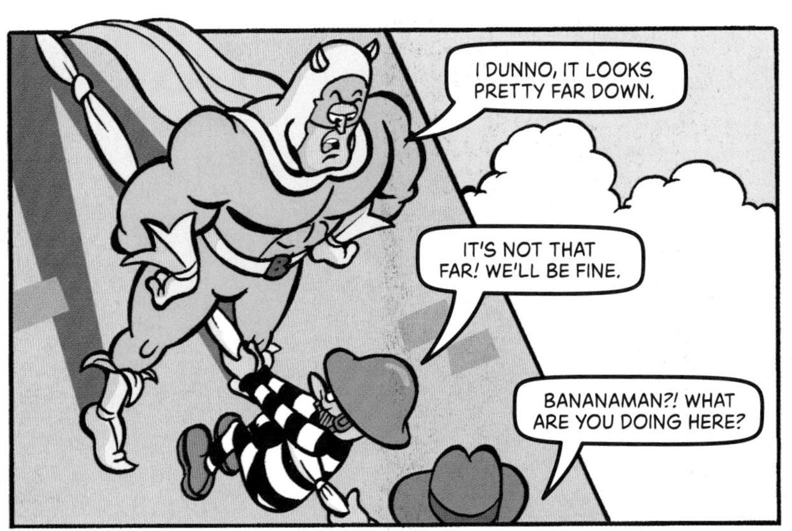
I DUNNO, IT LOOKS PRETTY FAR DOWN.
IT'S NOT THAT FAR! WE'LL BE FINE.
BANANAMAN?! WHAT ARE YOU DOING HERE?

DO YOU REALLY WANT TO KNOW HOW I'VE BEEN FINDING YOU SO EASILY?
TELL ME! PLEASE!
IT'S THE *LIVE VLOGGING*, ISN'T IT?

HUH?
WHAT?
YOU'VE SPENT ALL DAY BROADCASTING EXACTLY WHAT YOU'RE DOING!
ANYONE COULD JUST FOLLOW THIS TO SEE WHERE YOU ARE!

THIS VIDEO'S REALLY GOOD, BUT THIS IS THE FIRST TIME I'VE SEEN IT!
SO, YOU *DIDN'T* WORK OUT WHERE I WAS FROM MY VIDEOS?

NO, I WORKED OUT WHERE YOU WERE BECAUSE YOU DO THE SAME THING EVERY THURSDAY.
YOU TRY TO ROB A BANK, GO ON A ROBOT RAMPAGE, THEN ESCAPE FROM JAIL.

I DIDN'T REALISE I'D BECOME SO PREDICTABLE.
BEFORE YOU GO BACK TO PRISON, I HAVE A FAVOUR TO ASK YOU...

...CAN YOU TEACH ME HOW TO BE AN *AWESOME VLOGGER* LIKE YOU?
LATER...
HELLO, BANANA-FANS! WELCOME TO MY CHANNEL WHERE I RATE THE LATEST BANANAS!
GOOD WORK, BANANAMAN.
AND *THIS* IS BETTER THAN PRISON?!

DENNIS & GNASHER

THE WORLD'S WILDEST BOY... AND HIS BEST FRIEND!

AT THE TOP...
LOOKS LIKE THIS IS GOING TO BE THE EASIEST CHALLENGE!
TOO EASY?

WHO DARES PINCH MY APPLE?!
THAT'LL BE HESPERIDES! - ED

LIKE I SAID, EASIEST!
OH YEAH?
I CALL ON LADON!

WHO'S LADON? YOUR TINY BOYFRIEND?

OH... LADON'S A MANY HEADED DRAGON? I SEE!

I DON'T LIKE TO REPEAT MYSELF, AND WE RAN SCREAMING FROM THE OTHER TWO THINGS, BUT...

...ARRGH!

WE'LL BE FINE BEHIND THIS ROCK.

FOLLOW MY LEAD, BUDDY.

HI. I DON'T THINK IT'S TRUE WHAT THE OTHER HEADS SAY. YOU'RE NOT STUPID!
DON'T LISTEN TO THE OTHER HEADS, YOU'RE GNOT A WEIRDO!

LADON STARTS AN EPIC BATTLE WITH HIMSELF...
I'M NOT AN IDIOT!
ACTUALLY, YOU ARE!
WEIRD, AM I?
WELL, YES. A BIT!
I HOPE THAT COUNTS AS MISCHIEF!
WE'LL FIND OUT WHEN WE PICK THAT APPLE.
PICK
NOTHING HAPPENED. I GUESS IT DOESN'T COUNT!
I THINK YOU HAVE TO DO THE MISCHIEF WITH THE APPLE!
I PROBABLY HAVE TO DO THE MISCHIEF WITH THE APPLE... WHICH IS IMPOSSIBLE!
AH, WHAT A LOVELY DAY FOR A HILL WALK.
I MIGHT AS WELL GIVE UP. YOU CAN'T MENACE WITH AN APPLE!
I'M A BIT PECKISH.
I COULD HAVE A CEREAL BAR?
HERE, DO YOU WANT AN APPLE? I DON'T WANT IT.
THANK YOU.
I GUESS I FAILED.
WAIT... THAT APPLE'S GOLD!
CRUNCH!
OW! MY TEETH!
OW!
ALL RIGHT, SMARTY-PANTS! YOU DID IT! BUT YOU DON'T HAVE A HOPE OF BEATING THE FINAL CHALLENGE!
HA-HA! BRING IT ON!
POP
THE FINAL CHALLENGE IS STILL TO COME (LATER IN THE ANNUAL)! - ED

MENACE TEST III

Make your own catapult!

YOU'LL NEED

- 9 LOLLY STICKS
- 5 ELASTIC BANDS
- TEASPOON

1

Stack seven lolly sticks in a pile and wrap an elastic band round each end.

2

Join the other two lolly sticks together using an elastic band at one end.

3

Pull apart the two lolly sticks and push the seven lolly stick stack into the space between.

4

WARNING! Do not shoot these at people or animals, and only use outside!

Using the last two elastic bands, attach the spoon to the top lolly stick. Add some dried peas onto the spoon and let it fly! How far can you shoot?

MINNIE THE MINX

BACK IN THE GAME...
I WAS IN THE MIDDLE OF A QUEST SET BY WINCERIND THE WIZARD. WE NEED TO PREPARE FOR THE JOURNEY AHEAD!
I'VE FOUND TEN GOLD COINS AND A POTION OF SWIFTNESS! OOH, AND THE HEALING HANKIE OF HAGAAR!
BLITHER! I'M GONNA GET YOU WHEN I RESPAWN!

WHAT'S THIS QUEST THEN?
IT SEEMS WE'VE GOT TO RETRIEVE A MEDALLION OF POWER.
SOUNDS SIMPLE ENOUGH!

BUT WE'VE GOT TO RETRIEVE IT FROM THERE - THE MOUNTAIN OF MISERY! GULP!
COOL!

COME ON THEN, FRANCIS! LAST ONE TO THE MEDALLION IS A STINKY OGRE!
FOR THE LAST TIME, IN THE GAME I'M CALLED FRAN THE FEROCIOUS!

MINNIE THE LYNX AND FRAN THE FEROCIOUS EMBARK UPON THEIR QUEST...
PHEW! THIS EMBARKING UPON QUESTS IS HARD WORK!
YEAH!

OH NO! EMPIRE SOLDIERS! HOW WILL WE GET PAST?
WE CAN'T GO AROUND THEM WITHOUT HAVING TO BRAVE THE SWAMP OF UTTER GROSSNESS!
HMM...

RASP! CAN'T CATCH US, YOU STINKY SOLDIERS!

MIN! WHAT ARE YOU DOING?!
DON'T WORRY, FRAN! THOSE GUARDS ARE A BIT TIED UP AT THE MOMENT! CHUCKLE!

ACK!
TWANG!
HEY!
HO-HO! NICE ONE, MIN! THAT'LL GET US SOME EXTRA EXPERIENCE POINTS!
SO...
I'VE GOTTA ADMIT, I FEEL PRETTY GOOD ABOUT THIS QUEST NOW!
NOTHING CAN STOP US!
STOP RIGHT THERE, YOUNG LADY! YOU'RE SUPPOSED TO BE DOING HOMEWORK!
MR MAKEPEACE?!
DAD?! WHAT ARE YOU WEARING?!
I DON'T KNOW HOW TO CHANGE MY LOOK IN THIS GAME!
CLICK!
CLICK!
PRESS 'START', THEN 'OPTIONS', THEN 'APPEARANCE' THEN CHOOSE SOMETHING LESS ICKY!
HOW ABOUT THIS? DID IT WORK?
YIKES! JUST TAKE THIS AND COVER THAT BLUE BONCE OF YOURS!
MEANWHILE...
AHA! FOUND YOU, MINNIE! TIME FOR SOME PAYBACK!
OH! YOU'RE NOT MINNIE!
LEAP!
OOF!
HA-HA! LOOKS LIKE CRUNCHER HAS MIS-CRUNCHED!
CRUNCHER? GRR! COME HERE! YOU'RE IN BIG TROUBLE, YOUNG MAN!
THIS GAME IS THE BEST! CHUCKLE!
TEE-HEE! IT LOOKS LIKE THE TROLL HAS BEEN TROLLED! COME ON, FRAN! ADVENTURE AWAITS!

CALAMITY JAMES

THE UNLUCKIEST BOY IN THE WORLD!

Rubi
JJ
PIE FACE!
AT BEANOTOWN-ON-SEA...
NO-ONE'S EVER BEATEN IT, JJ.
MY BROTHER RECKONS SOMEONE MANAGED THE WHOLE MINUTE WITHOUT FALLING OFF.
I'VE HEARD THAT TOO, BUT IT'S JUST A SCHOOL LEGEND.
THIS YEAR I'LL BEAT THE BUCKING BRONCO! DEFINITELY.
BUCKING BRONCO
I'M JUST 60 SECONDS AWAY FROM BEING A NEW SCHOOL LEGEND!

PUT THE MONEY IN, PIE FACE.

BE AT ONE WITH THE BRONCO...

...AT ONE WITH...

...ARRGH!
I CAN'T WATCH!
CRASH
URRGH! I GOT A NASTY BUMP THERE.
ICE CREAM
DON'T WORRY - I'VE GOT SOME CREAM FOR THAT! YUM!

LATER, AT RUBI'S WORKSHOP...
IS THERE ANYTHING YOU CAN INVENT TO HELP KEEP ME ON THE BRONCO?
HMM...

SO...

AND...
BEHOLD - MY MAGNETO-PANTS!
OKAY. AND HOW WILL THEY HELP?
THE PANTS ARE MAGNETIC, SO THEY'LL BE ATTRACTED TO THE BRONCO'S METAL SKELETON. NO MATTER HOW IT MOVES, THE PANTS WILL STAY ON!
BETTER NOT GET TOO CLOSE TO ANYTHING MADE OF IRON, THOUGH.
CLANG!
BACK AT THE BRONCO...
PUT THE MONEY IN, PIE FACE.
OKAY-DOKEY!
IT'S WORKING, RUBI!
HOW LONG HAS IT BEEN?
45 SECONDS!
YEAH! WOO-HOO!
FIVE, FOUR, THREE...
ARRGH!
CRASH
DID I DO IT?
ICE CREAM
YOU WERE THROWN OFF WITH A SECOND TO GO...
URRGH!
...BUT THE MAGNETO-PANTS WILL GO DOWN IN SCHOOL LEGEND FOR STAYING ON THE FULL MINUTE!
GAH!

NUMSKULLS

The little guys that live in your head! Everybody has them!

THAT WENT FOR MILES.
DID YOU SEE WHERE IT LANDED, 'ERBERT?

OKAY, I ADMIT TODAY IS TURNING OUT LIKE ALL THE OTHER DAYS...
...BUT MAYBE THIS IS THE END OF THE BAD LUCK. LET'S GO OUT FOR SOME FRESH AIR.

JAMES IS WATCHING THE NEWS...
A GRUMPY TIGER ESCAPED BEANOTOWN ZOO EARLIER TODAY. IF ANY MEMBERS OF THE PUBLIC SEE IT, THEY ARE ADVISED TO RUN AWAY SCREAMING.
13

A RUNAWAY TIGER?! WHAT DO YOU THINK? IS OUR BAD LUCK OVER? SHOULD JAMES GO OUT FOR SOME FRESH AIR?
NO. IN FACT, LET'S GO BACK TO BED. THAT'S WHERE WE WERE BEFORE EVERYTHING STARTED GOING WRONG.

BUT...
TRIP!

TUMBLE!

INSIDE JAMES'S HEAD...
ARRRGH!!!

WE FELL UP THE STAIRS!
WHO FALLS UP STAIRS?!

LET'S JUST GET BACK TO BED!
CRAWL!

GRRRRR!
13

WHY WOULDN'T THE ESCAPED TIGER BE IN JAMES'S BED?!
?

MAYBE NOW'S THE TIME TO GET THAT FRESH AIR?!
ARRGH!!!
13

THE ORDINARY GIRL WITH THE EXTRAORDINARY BEST FRIEND!

'AT THE TOP OF THE JELLY BEANSTALK, HE BEHELD A MAGICAL KINGDOM...'
THIS GOING ON YETITUBE!
'YETI, ERM... SMELLED SOME JELLY BEANS. WHICH COULD TOTALLY HAPPEN!'
YETI SMELL JELLYBEANS!
OOH!
WORLD'S BEST GIANT
FEE-FI-FO... SPAGHETTI! I SMELL THE BLOOD OF AN ENGLISH YETI!
IT'S BEAN REAL PLEASURE, BUT YETI GO NOW!
AHA!
THIS NOT FAIRY TALE MORE A SCARY TALE!
'THEN THE GIANT GOBBLED YETI WHOLE!'
NOOOOOOO!
Little Minx
THE END! SO... WOULD YOU LIKE A JELLY BEAN?
Jelly Beans
NO! YETI NO LIKE JELLY BEANS ANY MORE!
SO...
GREAT! THAT'S ANOTHER JUNK FOOD ITEM CROSSED OFF THE LIST! TOMORROW, WE READ 'ALI BABA AND THE FORTY BISCUITS'. OR MAYBE 'GOLDILOCKS AND THE THREE ECLAIRS'!
HUH?
Ice Cream
Buns
Donuts
Pop
Crisps
Jelly Beans
Biscuits
Eclairs
Burgers
Chips
Cakes
HR

THE BASH STREET KIDS
THE CLASS EVERY TEACHER DREADS...
PART TWO!

IT'S PART TWO BUT WE STILL DON'T HAVE THE ANSWERS FROM PART ONE - SORRY!
IS SSSSSSOMEONE FEELING A LITTLE FLAT?!
GRR!

HELLO? CAN I HELP YOU?
GOOD DAY. I'M THE NEW SUBSTITUTE TEACHER.

SUBSTITUTE? I DON'T KNOW ANYTHING ABOUT A SUBSTITUTE! WHO ARE YOU REPLACING?
YOU! MWAH-HA-HA!

KAZAM!
WAAH! RIBBIT!

SO...
GOOD DAY, CLASS! DO SIT DOWN!
WHERE'S TEACHER?
AND WHO'S THIS SINISTER LOOKING GEEZER?
WHEN DID WE GET A FROG?
MAP

I AM PROFESSOR BALDYMORT. I'M AFRAID YOUR TEACHER HAS HAD TO, ER... HOP OFF FOR A WHILE. CHUCKLE!
HNNGGH! MY SCAR! YOWCH!
ARE YOU ALL RIGHT, HAIRY?
RUB!

I'M GETTING A BAD FEELING ABOUT THIS BALDYMORT... I FEEL A DARK AND EVIL FORCE WITHIN HIM!
WELL, HE IS A TEACHER!
WE'D BETTER KEEP AN EYE ON HIM!

TODAY'S LESSON IS ABOUT MAGIC. DO ANY OF YOU CHILDREN KNOW ANY MAGIC?
Magic
GULP!
I KNOW A TRICK, SIR! I CAN TURN THIS BIT OF PAPER...
FOLD!
FOLD!

ARRGH!
...INTO A PAPER PLANE!
TOSS!

PAPERPLANEUS VAPOURIS!
EVAPORATE!
FIZZ!
MY PLANE!
I KNEW IT! HE IS DARK AND EVIL!

QUICK! LEG IT!
COME ON, HAIRY!
RIGHT BEHIND YOU!

GOING SSSOMEWHERE, KIDSSS?
NAUGHTY CHILDREN! CHUCKLE!
HISS!
SLITHER!
LEAP!

LISTEN HERE, YOU WORMS. I KNOW ONE OF YOU IS HAIRY TROTTER! I DEMAND YOU HAND HIM OVER... OR ELSE!

SCRATCH!
I'M HAIRY TROTTER!
I'M HAIRY TROTTER AND SO IS MY SISTER!
AND ME!
RUB!
HUH? WHAT? GAH!

YOU WANT TO PLAY GAMES, EH? THEN I'M AFRAID THAT THE WHOLE CLASS IS SUSPENDED!
PUT US DOWN!
WHAT DO YOU THINK YOU'RE DOING?
FZZT!
FINE! I'M THE REAL HAIRY TROTTER! JUST LET THEM ALL GO!
LIFT!
RAISE!

THERE YOU ARE, TROTTER! FINALLY WE MEET! AND NOW YOU ARE GOING TO GIVE ME ALL OF YOUR POWER!
NEVER!
OOFYAH!
COLLAPSE!
FLOAT!
THUD!
SPLAT!

FINE! THEN I SHALL JUST TAKE IT MYSELF!
UH-OH!

THWOP!
HUH?
YANK!

NICE LASSOING, SPOTTY!
GRAB!
SNATCH!
HOW DOES THIS THING WORK? IS THERE AN ON SWITCH?
GRR! THOSE INTERFERING CHILDREN!

WHEN I GET THAT WAND BACK, I'M GOING TO TURN YOU ALL INTO FROGS, LIKE I DID YOUR TEACHER!
COME ON, DANNY! GET IT WORKING!
I'M TRYING! I'M TRYING!
I SHOULD DO SOMETHING!
RIBBIT!
GET THIS HORRIBLE THING OFF ME!
HURRY UP, DANNY!
I THINK I'VE GOT IT!
ER... ABRACADABRA?!
FWOOM!
HMPH! THIS DOES NOTHING FOR MY VILLAINOUS LOOK, BUT I'LL SURVIVE... UNLIKE YOU!
HE'S GOT HIS WAND BACK! THAT SPELLS TROUBLE!
ZIIP!
BOUNCE!
LEAP!
HEY, TEACH! YOU'RE LOOKING, ER... GREEN!
AND NOW, TO SHOW THAT I ALWAYS KEEP MY PROMISES, I'LL TURN YOU ALL INTO FROGS!
I DON'T WANT TO BE A FROG! I DON'T LIKE THE TASTE OF FLIES!
ROLL!
FROGTRANSFORMUS KIDDIUS!
BOUNCE BACK!
SHIELDUS PROTECTORUM!
WHOA! HAIRY CONJURED UP A SHIELD! IT'S SENT BALDY'S MAGIC BACK AT HIM!
RIBBIT?!
YUM! A TASSSTY LITTLE FROG!
SLURP! I FANCY SOME FROG'S LEGS!
LET ME TURN TEACHER BACK TO NORMAL! TEACHUS NORMALIUS!
RIBBIT! RIBBIT!
FWOOM!
EVERYTHING'S WRAPPED UP NICELY WITH NO LOOSE ENDS!
MEANWHILE, AT HOGLUMPS' SCHOOL OF MAGIC...
GERROFF!
SPLAT!
TWANG!
HEE-HEE! NOW THIS IS MAGIC! CHORTLE!
GOOD GRACIOUS! MY BEARD!
HELLO? BASH STREET SCHOOL? I THINK THERE'S BEEN A MOST AWFUL MIX-UP!
DS

You Will Need

A PAPER CUP

A WAND

A FRIEND WHO IS IN ON THE TRICK!

STEP 1

Make a hole in the back of the cup just big enough to push your thumb through.

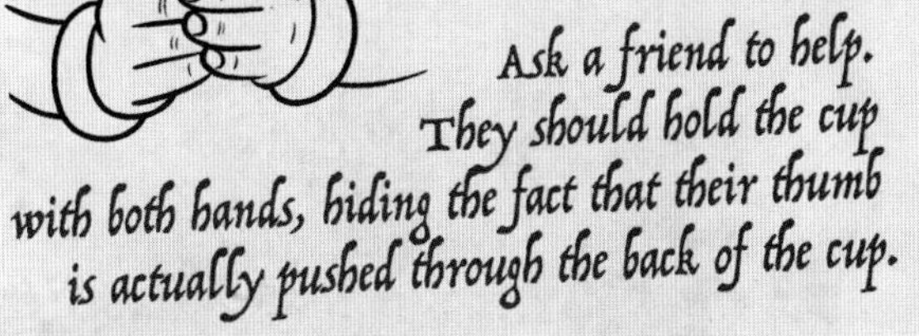

STEP 2

Ask a friend to help. They should hold the cup with both hands, hiding the fact that their thumb is actually pushed through the back of the cup.

STEP 3

Stand in front of your friend with the person you want to trick. Tell them you are going to make the cup levitate. Swish your wand and say the magic words "Floatarium Cupiosa".

STEP 4

Your friend should move their fingers away from the cup so it looks like it is floating - but really it's their thumb holding it up. Magic!

ROGER THE DODGER

HE'S ALWAYS GOT A TRICK UP HIS SLEEVE!

EVERYTHING OKAY, DAD?
YES, FINE. LET'S CONTINUE THE TOUR.
LOOK, ROGER. LOOK! IT'S ON LOAN FROM PARIS. IT'S LEONARDO DA VINCI'S 'MONA LISA'.
SHE LOOKS EXACTLY LIKE HOW I FEEL.
YAWN!
STAY BEHIND THE ROPE PLEASE, SIR.
OF COURSE. SORRY.
I NEED TO DRAW A LINE UNDER THIS TOUR WITH DODGE 982BU.
I'LL JUST SIT THIS ONE OUT ON THIS WEIRD CHAIR.
ROGER! WHAT ARE YOU DOING ON THAT CHAIR? IT'S FROM THE BAUHAUS!
BAUHAUS? BORE-HAUS MORE LIKE.
TRIP!
CRASH!
TAKE A SEAT, DAD.
GET OUT OF THAT CHAI... ARRGH!
YOU AGAIN! WHAT DID I SAY ABOUT NOT TOUCHING THE ARTWORK!
HEE-HEE! LOOKS LIKE DAD IS GOING TO HAVE A BRUSH WITH THE LAW.
SO...
I KNEW THIS GUY WAS GOING TO BE TROUBLE.
BUT I WAS FRAMED!
I LOVE IT WHEN LIFE IMITATES ART.

MINNIE THE MINX

FULL SPEED AHEAD!
ARRGH!
BRUM!

HE'S GOT A DECENT BIT OF SPEED FOR AN OLDIE!
HELP! OUT OF CONTROL CHAIR!

GOOD! I LIKE A MOVING TARGET. IT'S MORE OF A CHALLENGE.
HELP!

TRY ZIGZAGGING! I MIGHT MISS YOU WITH A FEW IF YOU DO THAT.
YOU'RE IN REAL TROUBLE NOW, YOUNG LADY!

TIME FOR A WELL-EARNED SNACK.
WHEN DID SHE HAVE TIME TO DO ALL THIS?

WHO CARES? I JUST NEED TO STAY AHEAD OF HER.
BEANOTOWN STADIUM

EXCUSE ME! SORRY TO BARGE THROUGH.
HE'S FASTER THAN ME!

HE'S FASTER THAN THIS RACEHORSE AS WELL, THANKS TO ME!
DO YOU MIND?!

HE'S EVEN FASTER THAN THESE RACING CARS! IT'S AMAZING HOW FAST SHEER TERROR CAN MAKE YOU RUN.
TODAY'S RACE IS CANCELLED BECAUSE IT'S EMBARRASSING TO BE SLOWER THAN AN OLD MAN AND AN ARMCHAIR.
BRING-BRING!
PUFF! WHEEZE! HELLO?
WHO WOULD PHONE AT A TIME LIKE THIS?
IT'S YOUR MUM. SHE WANTS ME TO GET SOME GROCERIES.
FINE. I'LL CHASE YOU TOWARDS THE SUPERMARKET THEN.
REMEMBER THE CARROTS AND GRAPES.
ARRGH! SLOW DOWN, MINNIE.
OKAY, OKAY! I GIVE UP. I CAN'T RUN ANY MORE.
widl
JUST AS WELL - WE'RE HOME.
YOU WERE RIGHT. IT IS BEDTIME. I'M A BIT TIRED AFTER ALL THAT CHASING.
YOU'RE TIRED?!
I'LL SLEEP FOR A WEEK.
BET HE WON'T! MINNIE'S FOUND A TROMBONE! - ED
FRAAAP!
ARRGH!

CALAMITY JAMES

THE UNLUCKIEST BOY IN THE WORLD!

WHEN LITTLE ERIC EATS A BANANA, HE BECOMES...
BANANAMAN
THAT'S WHAT YOU GET FOR TERRORISING BEANOTOWN, SQUID BREATH!
POW!
TRY THAT AGAIN, AND YOU'LL BE CALAMARI!
CRASH!
BEANOTOWN IS SAFE ONCE AGAIN.
ER... BANANAMAN?
YOU CAN THANK ME LATER, CHIEF O'REILLY. I'M BUSY DOING MY VICTORY SPEECH RIGHT NOW.
WHEN YOU WERE FIGHTING TO SAVE BEANOTOWN, YOU DESTROYED BEANOTOWN!
AND LOOK, HERE COMES MAYOR BROWN!
OOPS!
LOOK AT THIS DAMAGE! I'M MAKING SUPERHEROES ILLEGAL IN BEANOTOWN!
OH NO! THAT'S THE ONLY THING THAT I'M DRESSED FOR!
CHEER UP, BANANAMAN. YOU CAN STILL HELP BEANOTOWN. YOU'LL JUST HAVE TO BE A POLICE OFFICER NOW!
THANKS, CHIEF!
RIP!
ER... ONCE WE'VE FOUND A UNIFORM THE RIGHT SIZE FOR YOU!
THE NEXT DAY...
YOUR FIRST JOB AS A POLICE OFFICER IS TO DIRECT TRAFFIC!
MAKE SURE THAT THESE CARS KEEP MOVING SMOOTHLY.

WHICH SIDE OF THE ROAD DO WE DRIVE ON AGAIN?
YOU GO THERE! THE BIG CAR GOES, UM... THERE!
THAT CAR GOES FIRST BECAUSE IT HAS A FUNNY LICENCE PLATE!
PEEP!
TOOT!
BNO 15 GRB

I'M NOT ENTIRELY SURE HOW I DID THAT!

MAYBE BEING A TRAFFIC OFFICER WASN'T THE BEST FIT FOR YOU.

SO...
PART OF BEING A POLICE OFFICER MEANS HELPING THE COMMUNITY.
TRY ASKING IF ANYONE NEEDS HELP.

CAN I HELP YOU AT ALL?
OH YES, OFFICER! HOW DO WE GET TO THE BUS STATION?

IT'S NOT FAR AT ALL! I'LL FLY YOU THERE MYSELF!
WHOOSH!
ARRGH!

HERE WE ARE - BEANOTOWN TRAIN STATION. NO THANKS NECESSARY!
TRAIN STATION

WHY WOULD WE THANK YOU?!
THIS ISN'T THE BUS STATION!

AT BEANOTOWN POLICE STATION...
IS THERE ANY OTHER POLICE WORK I COULD DO?
NOT REALLY.

MAYBE I COULD HELP WITH THAT PAPERWORK?
THAT PAPERWORK IS JUST COMPLAINTS ABOUT *YOU!*

HOW ABOUT YOU GUARD THE TOWN HALL? THE MAYOR'S OFFICE IS HERE, SO IT'S VERY IMPORTANT!
SURE THING, CHIEF! WHAT SHOULD I DO?

DON'T DO ANYTHING! STAY HERE AND ***DON'T DO A THING!***
ESPECIALLY TRY NOT TO DO ANY DAMAGE!

THAT NIGHT...
DON'T DO ANYTHING? THIS IS EASY!
I WON'T EVEN STOP THE HEAVY MOB FROM STEALING THOSE THINGS!

HELLO, LADS!
ER, BYE... BANANAMAN!

THE NEXT DAY...
THE TOWN HALL WAS ROBBED LAST NIGHT! THEY STOLE EVERYTHING! INCLUDING THE TOWN HALL! WHY DIDN'T YOU STOP THEM?
I'M A POLICE OFFICER NOW, MISTER MAYOR. I HAVE TO DO WHAT MY CHIEF TELLS ME TO DO, AND HE TOLD ME TO DO NOTHING.

THAT IS TRUE, ACTUALLY!

YOU'RE MORE DANGEROUS AS A POLICE OFFICER THAN A SUPERHERO!
WHAT ELSE CAN I DO?

I THINK I MIGHT HAVE JUST THE JOB FOR YOU!

CRASH!
DEMOLITION MAN? I GET TO PULL DOWN OLD, UNSAFE BUILDINGS? I LOVE THIS JOB!
IF HE WAS GOING TO DO IT ANYWAY, I MIGHT AS WELL MAKE USE OF HIM!
SMASH!

BILLY WHIZZ The fastest boy in the world!

BIFFO THE BEAR Sillier than the average bear!

GNASHER & GNIPPER Beanotown's menace hounds!

LORD SNOOTY Beanotown's billionaire boy!

ROGER THE DODGER

HE'S ALWAYS GOT A TRICK UP HIS SLEEVE!

SO...
READY TO LEAVE, YOU TWO?
HEE-HEE!
DAD! ALIENS HAVE LANDED AND ARE TAKING OVER BEANOTOWN!
HA! I THINK YOU TWO HAVE BEEN PLAYING TOO MANY COMPUTER GAMES.
IT'S TRUE, MR DAWSON. LOOK!
ALIENS HAVE INVADED BEANOTOWN. I REPEAT, ALIENS HAVE INVADED BEANOTOWN!
IT'S ONE OF THEIR SPACESHIPS!
THIS CAN'T BE REAL.
THEY'RE TRYING TO COME IN THROUGH THE LETTERBOX!
ALIEN SLIME! WE'RE DONE FOR!
DO NOT GO OUTSIDE. STAY INDOORS. MAYBE PLAY A COMPUTER GAME AND WAIT FOR THIS TO ALL BLOW OVER.
I GUESS WE NEED TO STAY HERE.
SHAME. I WAS LOOKING FORWARD TO THAT TALK ABOUT PAPER CLIPS.
BUT...
NO! WE NEED TO GET OUT OF HERE AND RESCUE YOUR MOTHER!
OKAY, I WASN'T EXPECTING THIS!
THE ALIENS ARE COMING! WHERE ARE YOU?!
IT'S KIND OF ROMANTIC REALLY.
WHOOSH!
INSIDE DAVE'S HOUSE...
THERE'S NOTHING BETTER THAN A PAMPERING SESSION AFTER A HARD DAY'S RACING.
I HEAR YOU! THESE FACE PACKS ARE AMAZING.
WHY IS YOUR HUSBAND RUNNING DOWN THE STREET CARRYING OUR CHILDREN?
WHAT?!
WHAT ARE YOU DOING?!
ARRGH! THE ALIENS HAVE GOT YOU! WE'RE DOOMED!
ARGH!
WHAT ON EARTH HAVE YOU TWO BEEN UP TO?
NOW THAT'S WHAT I CALL A CLOSE ENCOUNTER!
I GUESS WE DON'T HAVE TO GO TO THAT TALK ABOUT PAPER CLIPS THEN.

THE BASH STREET KIDS
THE CLASS EVERY TEACHER DREADS...

WHERE ARE WE GOING, SIR?
DO YOU NEED US TO SET THE SATNAV?
I DON'T NEED THE SATNAV TODAY. I KNOW WHERE WE'RE GOING.

FIVE MINUTES LATER...
OKAY, WE'RE LOST. I NEED THE SATNAV, SPOTTY.
SIGH. WHAT'S THE ADDRESS?

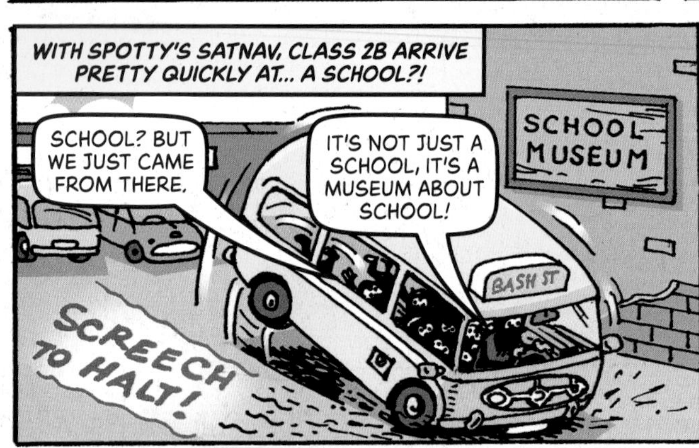
WITH SPOTTY'S SATNAV, CLASS 2B ARRIVE PRETTY QUICKLY AT... A SCHOOL?!
SCHOOL? BUT WE JUST CAME FROM THERE.
IT'S NOT JUST A SCHOOL, IT'S A MUSEUM ABOUT SCHOOL!
SCHOOL MUSEUM
BASH ST
SCREECH TO HALT!

WELCOME. THIS SCHOOL HAS BEEN STANDING FOR 100 YEARS AND IS IN A REAL CLASS OF ITS OWN!
GROAN!
CHUCKLE!
URRGH!

IN VICTORIAN TIMES, CHILDREN USED TO WRITE ON SLATES WITH CHALK. WE REALLY TAKE OUR TECHNOLOGY FOR GRANITE NOWADAYS!
THIS TOUR IS THE PITS! WE'VE HIT ROCK BOTTOM!
ANOTHER SCHOOL TRIP BITES THE DUST!

WHO'S THAT?
WHERE?

I DON'T SEE ANYONE. COME ON, WE'RE MOVING.
HUH! WHERE'D HE GO?!

NOW YOU CAN EXPLORE THE SCHOOL YOURSELVES.
LET'S GET A CUP OF TEA SO YOU CAN TEACH ME THOSE HILARIOUS SCHOOL PUNS!
THERE HE IS AGAIN! LOOK!
PORRIGE
BEANS

YOUR IMAGINATION IS PLAYING TRICKS ON YOU.
B-BUT HE WAS JUST THERE! I SWEAR!

POP!
ARE YOU TALKING ABOUT ME?
IT'S HIM! I KNEW I HADN'T IMAGINED IT!
WHO'S THAT?
HELLO, MISS!

POP!
HI! I'M JACOB, BUT YOU CAN CALL ME...

WHOOSH!
...THE JESTER!
WIGGLE!

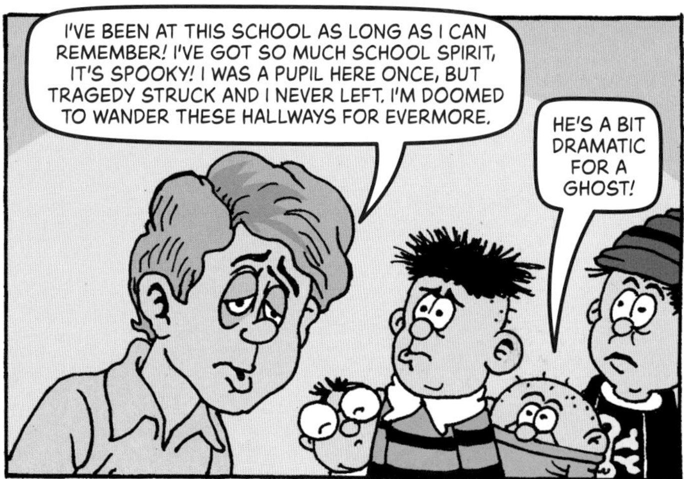
I'VE BEEN AT THIS SCHOOL AS LONG AS I CAN REMEMBER! I'VE GOT SO MUCH SCHOOL SPIRIT, IT'S SPOOKY! I WAS A PUPIL HERE ONCE, BUT TRAGEDY STRUCK AND I NEVER LEFT. I'M DOOMED TO WANDER THESE HALLWAYS FOR EVERMORE.
HE'S A BIT DRAMATIC FOR A GHOST!

THUD!
THUD!
I JUST LOVE...
I CAN HEAR HIM, BUT I CAN'T...

...PLAYING JOKES!
WAAH!

THAT GIVES ME AN IDEA OF HOW WE CAN CUT THIS VISIT SHORT!

I HEARD THIS PLACE IS HAUNTED.
WHAT A LOAD OF RUBBISH!
SHUFFLE!

TOSS!
WAAH!
CLICK!
EEK!
PONK!
TOLD YOU!

DID YOU FEEL AN ICY CHILL THERE? MUST BE *GHOSTS.*
SHRIEK!
FLOAT!
BLOW

SOMETHING'S GOT ME! SAVE YOURSELVES!
THIS PLACE IS HAUNTED!
LIFT!

ARRGH!
SCHOOL
RUN AWAY FROM THE GHOSTS!
EVERYONE ON THE BUS *NOW!*

CAN'T WE EVER VISIT SOMEWHERE THAT'S NOT HAUNTED, CURSED OR POSSESSED FOR ONCE?!
BASH ST.
ZOOM
VAROOM!

BACK AT BASH STREET...
IS THIS YOUR SCHOOL?
ARRGH!
BASH

HOW DID YOU GET HERE, JACOB?
I GOT CAUGHT UP IN THE CROWD AND THEN I WAS ON THE BUS WITH YOU. CAN I STAY HERE?

WE DON'T KNOW.
WE CAN'T KEEP A GHOST IN CLASS.
MOOOOOOAAAAAN! WAIL! WAAH!

WAIT! I HAVE AN IDEA!

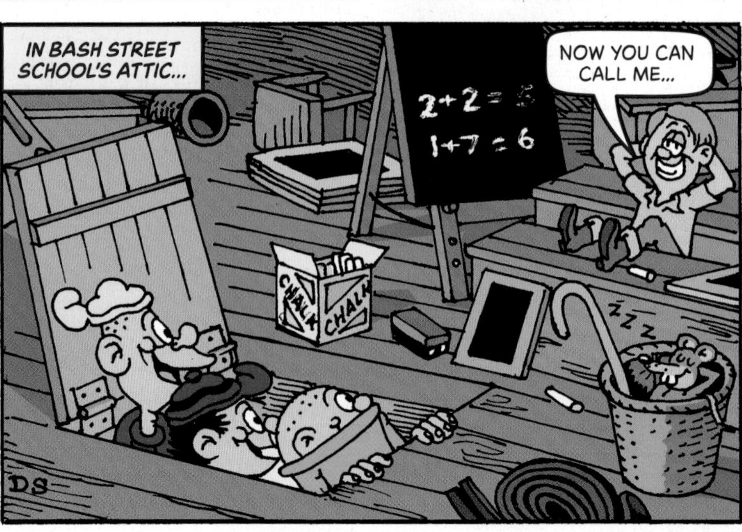
IN BASH STREET SCHOOL'S ATTIC...
NOW YOU CAN CALL ME...
2+2 = 5
1+7 = 6
CHALK
CHALK
DS

...THE *BASH STREET GHOUL!*

CAN YOU HANDLE MORE?
COMICS!
JOKES!
PUZZLES!
PRANKS!
HAPPY EASTER FROM SMIFFY

NUMSKULLS

The Little guys that Live in your head! Everybody has them!

IT'S UP TO YETI'S BRAINY NUMSKULL TO THINK OF A NEW PLAN...
EAT!
HOW DOES HE THINK UP THESE COMPLICATED PLANS?! - ED

YETI! IF THE QUEEN WERE HERE, WHAT WOULD SHE SAY?!
HOOVE!

BURP!
SHE WOULD NOT SAY THAT!

NOW THAT YETI HAS EATEN CUCUMBER, HIS NUMSKULLS GET TO TRY IT...
WHO-CUMBER?
GOO-CUMBER!

CAKE!
AFTER SANDWICHES, WE HAVE CAKE.

IN YETI'S HEAD...
CAKE!

GRASP!

BACK OFF!

THIS CALLS FOR AN EXTRA SPECIAL CLEVER PLAN...
CRY!
CRY!
CRY!

BLUB!
BLUB!

OKAY, YOU CAN HAVE A SLICE!
BIG SLICE!

SCOFF!!!
I GUESS THIS SLICE IS MINE THEN!

Rubi
JJ
PIE FACE!

IT'S CHRISTMAS EVE...
ARRGH! I'VE FORGOTTEN TO POST MY LETTER TO SANTA!
Santa

JINGLE!
JINGLE!
THAT'S THE JINGLE BELLS OF SANTA'S SLEIGH! MAYBE IT'S NOT TOO LATE!

YOU CAN DELIVER MY LETTER FOR ME, PAUL!

HURL!
DOOF!
WHAT WAS THAT?!

URRGH!
UH-OH.

SO...
PAUL DID WHAT?!
I'M COMING RIGHT OVER, PIE FACE!

I THINK THIS COULD PUT YOU ON THE NAUGHTY LIST!
NO! IT'LL BE MY FAULT PAUL DOESN'T GET ANY PRESENTS!
IT'S WORSE THAN THAT, PIE FACE. IF SANTA'S OUT COLD, NO-ONE WILL GET THEIR PRESENTS!

ARRGH!

IT'S UP TO US TO DELIVER THE PRESENTS.

UMM... WHERE DO WE START?

WE CAN'T JUST LEAVE SANTA HERE THOUGH!

GNNGH! I'M STARTING TO REGRET LEAVING *MINCE PIES* OUT FOR HIM EVERY CHRISTMAS EVE!
SAY WHAT?

WE ALWAYS LEAVE A PIE FOR SANTA AND A CARROT FOR RUDOLPH. DON'T YOU, PIE FACE?

HANG ON! IF THERE'S *THREE BILLION* KIDS IN THE WHOLE WORLD, AND THEY *ALL* LEAVE A PIE FOR SANTA...

...THERE'S NO TIME TO WASTE!

GO, RUDOLPH... GO, BLITZEN... GO, DONNA... GO, ER... *KEBAB!*
ZOOM!

CHRISTMAS MORNING...
I SEE THE CHRISTMAS DELIVERIES WERE A SUCCESS, PIE FACE.
HOW CAN YOU TELL?

NO REASON.
I NEED A BREAK! I DON'T EVEN *REMEMBER* DELIVERING ALL THOSE PRESENTS LAST NIGHT!

BETTY AND THE YETI!
THE ORDINARY GIRL WITH THE EXTRAORDINARY BEST FRIEND!

YOUR HOMEWORK ASSIGNMENT IS TO CHOOSE SOMETHING FROM THIS BOX OF TRINKETS AND DRAW IT AT HOME.
HEY! QUIT SHOVING!
GAH! THAT WOULDN'T HAVE HAPPENED IF I WASN'T SO SMALL.
I WONDER WHAT'LL BE LEFT?
URRGH! IT'S A WRINKLY MONKEY'S BUM!
IT'S ACTUALLY A PETRIFIED PEACH! A MAN IN EGYPT SOLD IT TO ME FOR A GOOD PRICE... THEN MAGICALLY DISAPPEARED.
AND YOU DIDN'T THINK THAT WAS ODD?! - ED

MEANWHILE...
YETI MEET BETTY AFTER SCHOOL.
KITTY!
MIAAAAOW!
SIGH... I WISH I WAS BIGGER.
SIGH... YETI WISH YETI NOT SCARY.

BUMP!
GLOW!
TSK! BE CAREFUL, YETI! YOU ALMOST BROKE MRS CREECHER'S MONKEY BUM!
GRUNT! YETI HUNGRY.
FRRRT!
GASP! WE'VE SWITCHED BODIES!
SNIFF! BLEURGH!

WITH MY NEW-FOUND STRENGTH, NO-ONE CAN PUSH ME AROUND!
SCRATCH!
OOH! A SALE ON PRINCESS COSTUMES!
YOU SHALL GO TO THE BALL
PLEASE ENTER THE STORE IN AN ORDERLY...
SALE
YES! I'M GONNA BE THE FIRST IN!
HEY! I WAS HERE BEFORE YOU. AND YOU'VE ALREADY GOT A COSTUME!
...ARRGH!
MEANWHILE, OUTSIDE...
KITTY!
AW! LOTS OF KITTIES.
TOO MANY KITTIES!
INSIDE THE SHOP...
OH NO! NONE OF THESE COSTUMES FIT ME NOW!
I WISH I WAS SMALL AGAIN.
YETI WISH HE NOT COVERED IN KITTIES.
BUMP!
GLOW!
PHEW! EVERYTHING'S BACK TO NORMAL. RIGHT, YETI?
MIAOW!
HR
COME ON, YETI. LET'S GO HOME.
MIAOW.
GRUNT! YETI HUNGRY!
UH-OH... - ED

MENACE TEST IV

Make a fizzy pop volcano!

YOU'LL NEED

- A BOTTLE OF FIZZY POP
- MENTOS

1

Find an open, flat space to create your volcano!

2

Open your fizzy pop bottle and put it on the ground.

3

Put the mento into the pop and run at least a few metres away from the bottle.

4

WARNING! Make sure you complete this task outside, as it is very messy!

Watch the pop explode like a volcano before your eyes!

DENNIS & GNASHER

THE WORLD'S WILDEST BOY... AND HIS BEST FRIEND!

UPSTAIRS...
I'VE GOT GOOD NEWS AND BAD NEWS.
THE BAD NEWS IS GNASHER'S BEEN TURNED INTO A THREE-HEADED MONSTER AND RUN OFF INTO TOWN, BUT THE GOOD NEWS IS I HAVE PROPER COFFEE SHOP COFFEE.
OOH! PROPER COFFEE!
OUTSIDE...
THIS WILL BE THE EASIEST CHALLENGE YET!
GNASHER'S MY BEST FRIEND. HE'LL PROBABLY HELP ME CATCH HIM!
BUT...
GNASH! GNASH! GNASH!
HA-HA! DID I FORGET TO TELL YOU I WIPED HIS MEMORY?
YES!
NIGEL PARKINSON

GNASH!
HEY! NOT ME!
WHY ARE YOU RUNNING?
CERBERUS IS A TERRIBLE, SLAVERING BEAST.
YOUR DOG IS SOMETHING ELSE ALTOGETHER!
PUT THIS LEAD ON HIM. THAT'LL COUNT AS CAPTURING.
HOW? HE HAS THREE HEADS!

SUDDENLY, GNASHER EATS DENNIS AND HERMES...
ARRGH!
CHOMP!
...BUT HERMES USES HIS POWERS TO ESCAPE!
NEVER LET US SPEAK OF THIS AGAIN!
POP!
AGREED!
YOU'RE ON YOUR OWN NOW!
POP!

HERMES MIGHT'VE WIPED GNASHER'S MEMORY, BUT I RECKON HIS TUMMY WILL REMEMBER THINGS EVEN IF HIS HEAD DOESN'T!
SOON...
THERE'S GNASHER!
HERE, BOY!

GRR!

GNASHER LOVES SAUSOS!
WHILE HIS TUMMY IS DISTRACTED BY THOSE, I CAN...
...GOT YA!
CLIP!
WHY HASN'T EVERYTHING RETURNED TO NORMAL?
BECAUSE YOU'VE CREATED NO MISCHIEF THIS TIME!
POP!
CHOMP!
HEY!
I GUESS EATING THE MESSENGER OF THE GODS COUNTS AS MISCHIEF. YOU WIN, DENNIS!
POP!
POP!
WOO-HOO! WHAT DO I WIN AGAIN?
THE GOLDEN JUMPER!
I GUESS I COULD SELL IT FOR...
NOT JUST GOLDEN BUT REAL GOLD!!!
YOU'LL DO NO SUCH THING!
YOUR CHALLENGES HAVE CAUSED LOADS OF DAMAGE TO THE TOWN!
THAT JUMPER SHOULD COVER THE BILL!
AT LEAST I PROVED I'M HISTORY'S GREATEST MENACE!
YOU DID INDEED! I'M ABOUT TO TAKE A HOLIDAY AND NEED SOMEONE TO COVER FOR ME. DO YOU THINK YOU'D LIKE GOD-LIKE POWERS TO PLAY TRICKS ON HUMANS?
YOU'RE NOT GIVING DENNIS POWERS!
YIKES! OKAY!
THE END!

EVERYONE WE KNOW LOVES BEANO

This book belongs to:
BASH STREET SCHOOL
SIMPER FUNGUS